WEST LAKE
A COLLECTION OF FOLKTALES

西湖民間故事

王健 書

合譯

插圖

WEST LAKE
A COLLECTION OF FOLKTALES

Translated by Jan and Yvonne Walls
Illustrated by Cheng Shifa

Joint Publishing Co., Hongkong
1983

Joint Publishing Co. (Hongkong Branch)
9 Queen Victoria St., Hongkong

First published 1980
Second printing 1983

Printed in Hongkong by
C & C Joint Printing Co. (H.K.) Ltd.
75 Pau Chung St., Kowloon, Hongkong

ISBN 962.04.0054.2

To Eileen

Contents

Introduction

The Chinese proverb says: "There is Heaven above, and there are Suzhou and Hangzhou below." The reference, of course, is to the beautiful scenery and environment, both natural and man-made, of the two cities. Hangzhou, with a history of more than two thousand and one hundred years, is today the capital city of Zhejiang Province, and has long been a center of cultural, political and literary activities. It was also the garden city of ancient emperors. The Wu Yue period, for a large part of the tenth century, was a golden age for its capital Hangzhou. During the Southern Song (A.D. 1127-1279), Hangzhou again became a capital, this time renamed Lin'an, and it grew into a major trading center. Marco Polo, who visited China in the late thirteenth century at the beginning of the Yuan Dynasty, was one of the first Westerners to call at Hangzhou, and he left the world with an impressive description of the city. The Qing Emperors Kangxi (reigned 1662-1722) and Qianlong (reigned 1736-1795) are each said to have visited Hangzhou six times. Hangzhou is today a modern city, retaining its famed beauty and boasting fairly developed industries.

The Qiantang River is located to the southeast of Hangzhou. In the past, high tide at the estuary often posed a threat to the city and its agricultural lands, and conservation was a continuous struggle. More effective measures have been used to control the destructive force of the Qiantang waves, and today the Qiantang tidal bore is a natural wonder that people come from all over to view. It is said that the best time to view the tidal bore is on the eighteenth day of the eighth month on the lunar calendar. The tide comes racing up the river and reputedly can reach a height of thirty feet. The roar of the approaching tide can be heard for more than half an hour before it passes the viewer.

Situated to the west of Hangzhou, and taking its name therefrom, is West Lake, or *Xi Hu*, perhaps the most famous lake in China. In the past, when the waters of the Qiantang River flooded the city, West Lake acted as a natural reservoir. It has had different names throughout history: Brilliant Sage *(Mingsheng)* Lake, Golden Ox *(Jinniu)* Lake, and Supreme *(Shang)* Lake.

The famous Song poet-official Su Dongpo (Su Shi, A.D. 1037-1101) once compared West Lake to Xi Shi, the famous beauty of ancient times. Geographically, the lake is situated at a place where plains, hills and waters meet, creating the ideal conditions for scenic beauty. Throughout history, its landscape has been fashioned both by natural and by human forces, but gradually the traces of human effort have merged with the natural lineaments. Since ancient times, pagodas, pavilions, bridges, causeways, and monasteries have been built to enhance its attractiveness and convenience for human activity. Among the many scenic spots are Bao Chu Pagoda, with its small base and very tall body; Three Pools Mirroring the Moon; Jade Spring, whose water spills into a square pool filled with colorful carp; Fly-in Peak, which is covered with Buddhist statues; Six Harmonies Pagoda, an octagonal structure built entirely of wood; Soul's Retreat Monastery, which was first established in the fourth century, most recently restored in 1956; and many others.

With a background of so much history, traditionally acclaimed beauty, and social activity, the imaginative powers of the folk in this area naturally created a wealth of folktales. In the spring of 1959, a group of people, with Xu Fei, Chen Weijun and Shen Tuqi in the lead, began collecting folktales in Hangzhou and the West Lake area. Altogether they gathered nearly four hundred stories of various kinds, and eventually selected these thirty-four tales for a volume that would give prominence to the scenic beauties of the area. The draft of the collection was finished in 1960, but the book *Xi Hu Minjian Gushi (West Lake: A Collection of Folktales)* was not published until 1978. We do not know to what extent these folktales have been edited, but we are told that they have been selected, sorted out and edited many times. The original collection was beautifully illustrated by Cheng Shifa, and these illustrations have been retained for this English edition.

Nearly all the thirty-four tales center around the well-known scenic spots and tell of their origins. The other few are anecdotes of famous figures who have been to West Lake, such as Yuchi Gong, Su Dongpo, and Emperors Kangxi and Qianlong. Whether the tales be supernatural, legendary or anecdotal, they are all told with great sincerity and charm.

West Lake, possessing such magnificent features, could only have been created in Heaven after much labor by mythical creatures like the dragon and the phoenix, as recounted in "The Bright Pearl." This is the folk way of explaining the almost supernatural beauty and purity of the lake. "Stone Man Ridge," on the other hand, describes the origin of the lake from a more human and down-to-earth point of view; here we find the lake was created only after much human hardship, labor and sacrifice. These two stories viewed together illustrate the attempt to use both supernatural and human efforts to explain the origin of West Lake.

The dragon and the phoenix, especially the former, appear frequently in the stories. We note that in both "Rising Sun Terrace" and "Phoenix Mountain," the phoenix is a beneficent bird and a supernatural helper who also assists in delivering humans out of miserable circumstances. The dragon, with the exception of the malevolent old fire dragon in "The Little Yellow Dragon," is almost always a beneficent being. He helps the underprivileged, as in "The Little Yellow Dragon" and "The Hua Pond"; or provides water, as in "Jade Spring" and "The First Well Spring of Mount Wu." The Dragon King may occasionally cause trouble, but when he is threatened or reasoned with, we feel that he is capable of understanding human needs. The story of the black dragon draws sympathy from the readers. The very fact that a dragon can transform into a person, and a person into a dragon, brings the relation between dragon and mankind even closer together. Both dragon and phoenix, then, are closely involved with human fate. These stories tend to substantiate Wen Yiduo's suggestion, in his *Myth and Poetry (Shenhua Yu Shi),* that the dragon and the phoenix were two totems of ancient Chinese peoples.

The Dragon King, as we see in "Six Harmonies Tries to Fill the River," "Beating the Dragon King" and "Prince Qian Shoots the Tide," also appears as the personification of a force of nature, namely the Qiantang tide. As mentioned before, high tide at the Qiantang River had been difficult to control, and often led to loss of agricultural lands. In many cases, however, human efforts may prevail over the forces of nature. Six Harmonies subdues the

Dragon King by throwing rocks into the river, and by cursing him. Prince Qian has thousands and thousands of arrows shot into the river to quell the ill-tempered Dragon King. The giant Great King Qian -- a magnified personification of human force — makes the Dragon King promise to give a loud warning before his tide rises. Thus, Six Harmonies, Prince Qian and the giant gained the approval and admiration of the people and they are commemorated in folklore to this day.

The destructive forces of nature are by no means all that the people have to confront. Another destructive force comes from within human society itself, through the arbitrary and selfish acts of the rich and the powerful. This is especially evident in unfeeling landlords and greedy, selfish officials. The victims of these people can be the populace in general, as in "Golden Ox Lake"; or the poor tenant farmers, as in "The Hua Pond"; or a kind and capable young woman, as in "Xing Chan"; or even a monkey, as in "Monkey Calling Cave." In the end, however, evil is always punished, often through supernatural intervention. This theme runs through almost all the tales.

But if evil officials are condemned by the folk, then good and benevolent ones are certainly praised and tribute is paid them. Yue Fei, a Song Dynasty general, is an embodiment of loyalty and bravery for the folk. Qin Hui, the Prime Minister who caused Yue Fei's death, is considered "foul" and his likeness was fried in oil and eaten. This is the folk way of expressing partiality and admiration towards a "good" general. Su Dongpo is an exemplary good "fatherly" official in the eyes of the folk. In "Su Dongpo Solves a Case by Painting Fans" and "Dongpo Meat," we hear the people lament his unjust punishment and express their sincere love for him. In their stories, the folk redress his wrongs by emphasizing his sense of justice and his concern for the common people, making it clear that he was a good man victimized by the intrigue of jealous officials.

Among the heros most celebrated in the tales are those who suffer long and even sacrifice their lives for the public good. There are many of them: Bao Chu who finds the captive sun; the little yellow dragon who leads the people against the old fire dragon; and Waterboy who brings a source of water to the people. The most celebrated heroines, typically, are model mothers, wives, daughters-in-law and good neighbors, such as Lady Wisdom, Xing Chan and Lady White.

Love stories always occupy an important position among folktales. In this collection, "Lady White" and "A Thread of Sky" are two beautiful and touching stories that let the reader experience the joys and sorrows of the lovers. What is more, we are given to believe that love can even transcend human form. Despite the fact that Lady White is the transformation of a snake, Xu Xian loves her to the end, and her love for Xu Xian is always true. In the other tale, the love between Stone Child and Sister Flower persists even after they both have been transformed into birds.

Humor and satire are two other elements we find in several stories. Mad Monk in "Fly-in Peak" is reminiscent of the crude monk Lu Zhishen in the epic *Water Margin*. When Mad Monk steals the bride and lures the whole village to run after him with various "weapons" in their hands, the reader cannot help but laugh at the whole incongruous scene. When the Governor in "Monkey Calling Cave" cries out in exasperation: "This one doesn't count!" after he is defeated at chess by a golden-haired monkey, we have to laugh at both the ridiculous situation and the Governor's vanity and false pride. When Yuchi Gong first gives the monk Immortal Forest a taste of his own medicine, and then assigns him a spot for his gate far away from his monastery, we laugh with satisfaction and agree that the monk deserves every bit of what he gets. In another story, we see a man ride unannounced into the yamen on the back of a donkey in a most unassuming manner, and only when he shows his Imperial seal do we learn that he is none other than the new Governor, Su Dongpo. The whole unexpected and incongruous scene is a good example of how folktales handle humor. Emperors are "Sons of Heaven"; in polite society they are not to be ridiculed. The folk, however, see them as ordinary human beings with human foibles and they are made the objects of satire. Emperor Kangxi demonstrates himself capable of making mistakes, but he can only defend himself by the unreasoning shout of "Silence!" Emperor Qianlong, so anxious to trap Monk Censure with a mistaken utterance, only ends up making a complete fool of himself. In "Eight-trigram Plot," the Emperor's deceitful act is uncovered by a mere old farmer. These reverend Emperors are satirized here and we are given to feel that they were taught a lesson.

The carvings and statues on the mountains in the West Lake area clearly show that stone craftsmanship used to be an important trade. It is interesting to learn from "The Stone Censer" that Lu Ban — commonly considered the ancestor of carpentry — and his sister are the master craftsmen who taught people here the art of stone-cutting. Waterboy, Stone Child and the old stone cutter in "Plum Blossom Monument" are other examples of the excellent stonecraftsman ideal.

Tea, silk and embroidery are still very important products of this area even today. Dragon Well *(Long Jing)* Tea has been famous for ages, because the leaves are beautifully shaped, and the tea is fragrant and mellow. "The Ancestors of Tea" recounts the almost accidental origin of the cultivation of this famous tea, and how it came about as a reward for an old granny's good deeds. "Lady Silkworm" tells a charming story of the origin of sericulture. Sister Flower in "A Thread of Sky" and Autumn Lass in "Phoenix Mountain" excel in embroidery with such good skills that the things they embroider are life-like.

These thirty-four stories offer us imaginative insights which can increase our understanding of the spirit of the historical place and its people, their feelings and their day-to-day activities.

While these folktales exhibit strong local characteristics, they also show clearly universal traits. For example, in a typically Chinese tale like "Rising Sun Terrace," where the son continues and completes his father's unfinished task with the encouragement of his faithful mother, we detect elements of the universal hero syndrome. The circumstance of the hero Bao Chu's birth is unusual, for he is born when his mother is grief-stricken on the discovery of her husband's death. His childhood and growth are unusual: "The boy began to grow as soon as the wind blew on him. When the wind first blew, he could talk. The second time the wind blew on him, he could already run. The third time, he grew into a strong man, eighteen feet tall." When he learns about the death of his father, he voluntarily sets out on the quest for the lost sun. A magic helper, the shining golden phoenix, comes along on the adventure. On the road, other helpers, villagers, make him a "hundred families' coat" which will later save him from being frozen to death. Then the first hero test: He has to swim across a wide and treacherous river. More helpers, other villagers along the way, offer him a bag of soil which will enable him to reach the dark world of the demons. He comes upon another village where he is tempted by fat men and beautiful ladies, good food and fine wine. When he discovers that these villagers are all demons in disguise, he flees. After successfully enduring further trials, he comes to a distant sea and discovers the underwater cave where the demon king has hidden the captive sun. After doing battle with the demon king, Bao Chu rescues the sun and pushes it halfway up through the sea, but he dies of exhaustion. His supernatural helper the phoenix carries the sun back up into the sky, and light and warmth are restored to the world in a blaze of glory.

One of the milestones in the study of world folklore was the publication in 1932 of Stith Thompson's *Motif-Index of Folk-Literature* (Bloomington, Indiana, 1932-1936). In this monumental work, Thompson isolated the main narrative elements recurring in folk-literature around the world, then systematized and numbered them as motifs. It has since become one of the most important reference tools for anyone who studies folk-literature. All of the thirty-four folktales in the present collection contain some of these world-wide motifs. Consideration of these elements together with those that are typically Chinese should add more to the reader's appreciation of the stories in this collection. With this in mind, we append to the main body of stories a list of motifs, according to their order in *Motif-Index of Folk-Literature* (Revised ed., Indiana University Press, 1955), with the corresponding titles of the folktales in which they appear. We also include a list of place names mentioned in the stories, with *pinyin* romanization and Chinese characters for convenient reference.

We hope that these folktales will be of interest to students of folklore and to those readers who simply enjoy good stories.

Jan and Yvonne Walls

Victoria, B.C.
September, 1979

The Bright Pearl

It was said in ancient times, in a cave east of the Milky Way, there lived a snow white jade dragon; and in the big forest west of the Milky Way, there dwelt a colorful gold phoenix. The jade dragon and the gold phoenix were neighbors. Every morning, one would emerge from the cave and the other fly out of the forest. After a simple greeting to each other, each would then hurry off to do the day's work.

One day, while one of them was flying in the sky and the other was swimming in the Milky Way, they suddenly came upon a fairy islet. On the islet, they discovered a bright and shining stone. The gold phoenix liked it very much: "Jade Dragon! Look, Jade Dragon! What a beautiful stone!"

The jade dragon was also attracted to it: "Gold Phoenix! Shall we work on it and make it into a pearl?"

The gold phoenix nodded her head in agreement, and they started to work on it.

The jade dragon clawed it with his claws and the gold phoenix pecked at it with her beak. They worked on it day after day and year after year, until finally they fashioned it into a round, bright pearl. The gold phoenix was so pleased that she flew to the fairy mountain and brought back many dew drops to sprinkle upon the pearl. The jade dragon was so happy that he swam to the Milky Way and brought back great quantities of pure water to spray over it. After much sprinkling of dew and spraying of pure water, it gradually became a bright and shining pearl!

From then on, the jade dragon grew to like the gold phoenix and the gold phoenix liked the jade dragon. Both of them loved their pearl. The jade dragon did not want to go back to the cave east of the Milky Way any more, and the gold phoenix had no desire to return to the forest west of the Milky Way; therefore they stayed on the fairy islet in the middle of the Milky Way and kept watch over their own pearl day and night.

Now, this bright pearl was a real treasure. Wherever the bright light of the pearl might shine, the trees there would be green forever, the hundred flowers would bloom all together, the mountains would be bright, the waters beautiful and there would be a bumper harvest of all the grains.

One day, the Queen Mother of the West walked out of her palace gate and saw the beautiful shining light of this pearl. She loved it so much that she ordered a trusted heavenly soldier to steal it at night. Once, when the jade dragon and the gold phoenix were soundly asleep, the heavenly soldier quietly stole the pearl away from them. The Queen Mother of the West was overjoyed when she obtained this pearl. She loved it so much that she would not even let anyone see it, but hid it in the palace. She closed it behind nine layers of gates, which were locked with nine locks.

When the jade dragon and the gold phoenix woke up and discovered that their pearl had disappeared, they were worried sick! They looked for it in the east, and searched in the west. The jade dragon searched in every cave under the Milky Way, and the gold phoenix looked in every corner of the fairy islet, but still they could not find it, and they were extremely saddened. Nevertheless, they continued to search for it day after day, and night after night, hoping to find it some day.

On the day the Queen Mother of the West celebrated her birthday, immortals from all directions came to celebrate in her palace. The Queen Mother arranged for an "immortal peach party" to entertain all the immortals. They were all drinking fine wine, eating the immortal peaches, loudly singing happy birthday to her: "May your fortune be as great as the Eastern Sea is deep; may your life be as long as South Mountain is high!"

All of a sudden the Queen Mother of the West became so happy that she told all the immortals: "My friends! I am going to show you a precious pearl. It is one the likes of which you may find neither in heaven nor on earth!"

So saying, she took the nine keys from her sash and opened the nine locks. She entered the nine gates and brought out that bright pearl. She held it on a gold platter and placed it in the middle of the big hall. The pearl gave out a bright and glittering light. When the immortals saw this, they all praised it, shouting with glee.

At this very moment, the jade dragon and the gold phoenix were still looking everywhere for the pearl.

When the gold phoenix noticed the cold bright light given out by the bright pearl, she shouted to the jade dragon immediately: "Jade Dragon! Hurry and look! Isn't that the cold bright light that comes from our pearl?"

The jade dragon poked his head out of the Milky Way and took a look: "You're right! It must be our pearl. Let's hurry and get it back!"

The jade dragon and the gold phoenix followed the light and came all the way to the palace of the Queen Mother of the West.

Just at this moment, the immortals were standing around the pearl and admiring it. The jade dragon rushed forward: "This is our pearl!" The gold phoenix also said: "This bright pearl belongs to us!"

When the Queen Mother of the West heard this, she was enraged. She rushed towards the jade dragon and the gold phoenix and shouted at them: "What nonsense! I am the true mother of the Jade Emperor. All the treasures in heaven belong to me!"

When the jade dragon and the gold phoenix heard this, they also became angry: "This pearl was not born of heaven nor grown on earth. It was ground and pecked out by us with much hard work day after day and year after year!"

Hearing this, the Queen Mother of the West was both embarrassed and enraged. She stretched out her hands to protect the gold platter that was holding the pearl. At the same time, she ordered the heavenly soldiers and heavenly generals to drive away the jade dragon and the gold phoenix. When the gold phoenix saw that the Queen Mother was going to be so unreasonable, she rushed forward to grab the pearl. When the jade dragon saw that the Queen Mother was so unreasonable, he too rushed forward to grab it. Thus three pairs of hands grabbed hold of the gold platter, and none of them would let go of it. They pulled back and forth, and the gold platter swayed from one side to the other. Finally, the bright pearl rolled off the platter, down onto the stairs, and rolled from heaven on and on down towards the earth.

When the jade dragon and the gold phoenix saw that their pearl was rolling down towards the earth, they quickly rushed alongside to protect it. The jade dragon was flying, and the gold phoenix was dancing. Now they were in front of it, now behind it, always protecting their bright pearl. Slowly, so slowly, the pearl descended down to earth. This bright pearl had no sooner touched the ground than it became the pure and clear West Lake.

The jade dragon, unable to bear the thought of leaving his pearl, turned into the strong and tall Jade Dragon Mountain to protect it. The gold phoenix, also unable to bear the thought of leaving her pearl, turned into the green and lovely Phoenix Mountain to watch over it.

From then on, Phoenix Mountain and Jade Dragon Mountain have been standing quietly beside West Lake.

Even now, there are two lines of an ancient folksong that is still popular in Hangzhou:

> The West Lake pearl descended from Heaven,
> The dragon flew and the phoenix danced to Qiantang.

Golden Ox Lake

A long, long time ago, West Lake was called Golden Ox Lake.

At that time, this lake was just one vast expanse of plain water. Along the shores of the lake the soil was dark and fertile. People who lived nearby were all farmers, and they irrigated their fields with the lake water. When the rice plants bore ears, they were all full and round, like strings of pearls. When the farming was done, people would all go to the lake to fish or catch shrimp. They all got along well with each other, and they led a peaceful and happy life.

At the bottom of this lake there lived a golden ox. Whenever the sun shone for a long time, the waters of the lake would recede and the golden ox would appear. From afar, one could see his shining gold back, his raised head and the upright horns. Then the ox would spew out a huge mouthful of water, and the lake would immediately be filled to the brim again.

One summer, it hadn't rained for nine times nine, eighty-one long days. It was so dry that the bottom of the lake was bared to the sky, and the fields around the lake were dry as rocks. The cracks in the fields were several inches wide and the tender shoots of grain were all withered. People were all so parched that their eyes caved in their sockets, and they were strengthless and limp. They were longing for the appearance of the golden ox every day.

One morning, as everyone was standing by the lake, looking for the appearance of the golden ox, suddenly they heard the sound of "moo," and then they saw the golden ox come out, breaking through the dried mud. The ox shook his head several times, wagged his tail a little, then blew out a huge mouthful of water, and in no time at all, the lake was filled to the brim.

The people were so happy that tears began to run down their cheeks. Just as they were thanking the golden ox, it raised its head, and with a glint in its bright eyes, gave a "moo" and disappeared into the lake again.

The news of this incident soon spread all around. The local bailiffs passed it on to the yamen runners, and the yamen runners passed it on to the Magistrate of Qiantang County.

When the County Magistrate heard this, he held on to his belly, laughed and said, "What a living treasure! If I can present him to the Emperor, I'm sure I will be promoted and become rich!"

Right away he sent his yamen runners to go and catch the golden ox.

The yamen runners and the local bailiffs all hurried over to the lake, but all they could see was the vast expanse of plain lake water. Where could the golden ox be? They began to ask the local people. But when the people saw that they were from the local government, they either replied that they did not know, or they just silently slipped away. The yamen runners could do nothing but to go back and report the failure of their mission.

The County Magistrate was angry. Fondling his mustache, he thought and thought, until a wicked idea came to him.

He told his underlings: "If that's the case, you go and gather all the people to dry the lake. Kill anyone who refuses to come!"

All the people who lived by the lake — men and women, old and young — were driven to the lake. Under the coercion and threats of the County Magistrate, and with tears in their eyes, they started to draw the water from the lake.

Drawing and drawing, they took the water for nine times nine, eighty-one long days, until they were all worn out and exhausted. Finally, on the last day they had drawn all the water from the lake and the lake was dried up, and indeed, there was the golden ox, lying at the bottom of the lake. The glow of his body made the whole sky and earth bright.

The golden glow was so bright that the County Magistrate could not even open his eyes. However, he still went ahead and called for the runners to go to the bottom of the lake and seize the golden ox. Strangely enough, the ox seemed to be rooted to the bottom. They could not lift or move him no matter how hard they tried. The local people were all pleased, though they dared not show it.

When the County Magistrate saw that the golden ox could not be moved, he said to the people, "A reward of three hundred taels of silver to whomever can lift the golden ox!"

But none of the people made a move; they just ignored him in their anger.

When the County Magistrate noticed that the people were all ignoring him, he shouted angrily, "If the golden ox cannot be lifted up today, you will all be killed!"

Just as the County Magistrate finished uttering these words, the golden ox gave a roar as loud as a thunderclap in the blue sky. Then everyone saw sand flying and rocks rising. The earth quaked and the mountain shook. The County Magistrate was so scared that his face turned ashen white. He wanted to run away, but his legs went limp and could not even move a step.

At this moment, the golden ox stood up. With his round eyes shining bright, he raised his head and gave another roar. Then he spewed forth billows of white water which rushed directly towards the County Magistrate and his yamen runners. All were carried away by the huge waves.

Immediately, the lake was filled with water again.

From that time on, the golden ox in the lake never appeared again and the water in the lake has never dried up since.

People could not forget the golden ox. They built a high tower on top of the city wall by the lake and climbed up on it everyday to look for the appearance of the golden ox. This tower then later came to be known as "Surging Gold Gate."

Rising Sun Terrace

A long, long, long time ago, at the foot of Gemstone Mountain by West Lake, there was a small village. A young husband and his wife lived in this village. The man was called Liu Spring, and his wife Lady Wisdom. He farmed and she wove cloth. They worked hard and lived frugally, so their lives were sweet and happy, and people throughout the village all praised them as an ideal couple.

One morning, a colorful dawn glow appeared in the east: the bright red sun was rising. Liu Spring picked up his hoe to go work in the fields; Lady Wisdom tidied up her silk, making ready to sit at the loom to work. At this moment, suddenly a wild gale rose up, and black clouds unfolded and came rolling in the sky. The sun that had just risen now sank down and disappeared.

From then on, the sun never rose again, and when the sun stopped coming out, the world became dark and cold. The trees no longer greened, flowers no longer reddened, and the crops would not grow. All the wicked ghosts and demons took advantage of this darkness to come and do their evil deeds. How could anyone go on living? People began to worry.

Where, then, could the sun have gone? Only the Elder who was one hundred and eighty years old knew the answer. He said that there was a demon king who lived under the sea and commanded many lesser demons; these demons feared the sun more than anything else. It must have been this demon king who had robbed the people of the sun.

Liu Spring was very much saddened to see the people living in such complete darkness. Everyday, he groped through the darkness to visit and console every household in all the villages. When he visited a family, they would say: "Liu Spring! We are freezing to death without the sun!" When he went to see another family, they would tell him: "Liu Spring! Without the sun, we are all going to starve!" When Liu Spring heard this, his heart ached as if it had been stabbed by knives.

When he went home, he said to his wife: "Lady Wisdom! Without a sun, the people of the world are suffering from cold and starvation. I plan to go search for the sun and bring it back again!"

Hearing this, Lady Wisdom thought for a while: "If you really want to, you should go and I'll not detain you. Don't worry about things at home. When you have found and brought back the sun, people will be able to live well again."

Lady Wisdom cut off a strand of her long hair, mixed it together with hemp and made a pair of sandals for her husband. She also made a thick cotton padded jacket, and asked Liu Spring to take it along. She saw her husband to the gate, then suddenly a bright golden light flashed on the horizon, and a golden phoenix flew over from afar and settled on Liu Spring's shoulder.

Liu Spring patted the phoenix: "Golden Phoenix! Come along with me. Let's go and find the sun!" The golden phoenix turned her eyes about a few times and nodded her head.

Liu Spring took hold of Lady Wisdom: "My dear, if I cannot find the sun, I will not come back. But if I should die on my quest, I will become a bright star to point out the way for future generations!" And so saying, he left with the golden phoenix.

Lady Wisdom climbed to the top of Gemstone Mountain in the dark every day to look for her husband. Longing, gazing, she did not know how much time had passed, but the world was still as black as ink. There was not a single ray of sunshine.

One night, Lady Wisdom suddenly saw a bright shining star shoot up and hang in the sky. After a little while, the golden phoenix flew back with downcast head and stopped by her feet. As soon as Lady Wisdom saw this, she knew that her husband had died on the journey. She was so grief-stricken that she fainted and fell to the ground.

By the time Lady Wisdom woke up, the child she had been carrying was already born. This boy began to grow as soon as the wind blew on him. When the wind first blew, he could talk. The second time the wind blew on him, he could already run. The third time, he grew into a strong man, eighteen feet tall. When Lady Wisdom saw this, she became extremely happy. She gave the boy a name, and called him Bao Chu.

Lady Wisdom took Bao Chu home. As she looked at her son, she thought of her husband, and her tears came trickling down beyond her control.

When Bao Chu saw this, he asked: "Why are you crying, Mama?"

Lady Wisdom could not control her sadness, and she told him about his father, and how he had died on his way to find the sun.

"Mama, let me go and find the sun!"

Lady Wisdom looked at her son, and she could not bear to part with him. However, she knew that people would always suffer as long as there was no sun and this had to be stopped. As she thought of this, she nodded her head and agreed.

Lady Wisdom once again cut off a strand of her long hair and mixed it with hemp to make a pair of sandals for her son. She also sewed a very thick cotton padded jacket for Bao Chu to wear.

When Bao Chu walked to the gate, the shining golden phoenix flew over again and stopped on his shoulders.

Lady Wisdom pointed to the bright star in the sky: "My son, after your father died, he transformed into that star. Just walk in the direction the star is pointing, and you'll not lose your way."

Bao Chu nodded his head.

Pointing to the golden phoenix, she again said: "This golden phoenix accompanied your father in his search for the sun before. You go with her again!"

Bao Chu nodded his head: "Mama, after I leave, no matter for how long, please never never feel sad for me. Once you shed tears, my heart will tremble, and I will never have the strength to search for the sun."

When the people in the villages heard that Bao Chu was going in search of the sun, they all came to see him off. Some brought clothes for him, and some brought dried food. They all accompanied Bao Chu for a long, long way.

Bao Chu started off with his golden phoenix. Undaunted by darkness and cold, he walked with all his might towards that distant bright star in the east. Walking on and on, he turned corner after corner; he climbed over one mountain after another. He climbed up eighteen cliffs and nineteen precipices. The bushes tore his jacket to shreds, and the ιorns pricked many wounds on his body, and he was eeding. His jacket became more and more tattered and the eather was getting colder and colder.

One day, Bao Chu walked into a village. When the llagers saw this traveller from a distant land, they all ιthered around him, and asked, "Where are you going?"

"I'm going to look for the sun!"

When they heard that another person was going to look ɔr the sun, they were overjoyed. They told him of this and f that and instructed him to be careful. When they saw ιat his jacket was so tattered, they each cut off one corner ːom their own jacket and made him a "hundred families' oat." Bao Chu felt their warmth from the bottom of his eart when he put on this "hundred families' coat," and he ɔ longer felt cold. He bade farewell to the villagers and ontinued on his way.

Bao Chu walked on and on without stopping. He swam ცross one river after another, and crossed over beach after ჟeach. One day, he came to the side of a great river that was ɔ wide he could not see to the far shore. Not even an eagle ːould fly across it. The waters of the river were so turbulent ιnd swift that even rocks as big as houses were easily swept ιway. The brave Bao Chu leaped into the river and started ːo swim towards the other shore with all his might, ːlenching his teeth together and holding his breath. Endless ധaves rushed toward him and beat against him, and whirlpools kept drawing him into their swirls, but still he kept swimming with all his might. Swimming on and on, it looked as if he was about to reach the other shore when suddenly a bitterly cold wind started to blow and the whole river froze over. Bao Chu was frozen solidly in the river and the golden phoenix seemed to have frozen to death on the ιce.

Since Bao Chu was wearing the "hundred families' coat,"

he could not be frozen to death no matter how cold it was. Slowly, the heat from his body began melting the ice around him. First, he held the golden phoenix tightly in his arms. Then he pounded his fists on the ice, and the ice in the river cracked into pieces. The water from the bottom of the river rushed towards Bao Chu, so he quickly jumped onto a block of ice, and then jumped from one piece to another until finally he was able to jump onto the other shore. After absorbing heat from Bao Chu's body, the golden phoenix came back to life.

Having crossed this river of ice, Bao Chu again came to a village. The villagers all surrounded him, and were pleased to hear that he was going to seek the sun. After learning how many difficulties he had encountered, they respected him all the more.

"My boy," a white-bearded old man said to him, "Our lives have become more difficult by the day since the sun disappeared. We really have nothing to give you, but each of us will offer a handful of our soil. This is soil that has been watered with our ancestors' sweat from generation to generation! Take it with you, you may find it useful."

The old man brought a bag and every person in the village picked up a handful of the soil and put it in the bag. When the bag was filled, they gave it to Bao Chu.

Bao Chu carried this bag of soil on his shoulder and continued traveling towards that bright star in the east. Traveling on and on, he climbed over ninety-nine tall mountains and swam across ninety-nine wide rivers, then came to a three-forked road. He did not know which road to follow.

Just as he was worrying about which road to take, an old lady came over to him from the roadside. "My boy, where are you going?" she asked.

"I am going to look for the sun!"

Rising Sun Terrace

"Looking for the sun? It's still a long way. I would say you should turn around and go back home!"

"I don't care how far it is or how hard the road is, I must go and find the sun. I'll never go back home if I can't find it!"

Hearing this, the old lady pointed to the right: "If you follow this road, you'll find the sun. There is a village not far from here. You should stop there to take a rest."

As Bao Chu was talking to the old lady, the golden phoenix kept rushing at her angrily, beating her with its wings, clawing at her face, and pecking at her eyes. Bao Chu thought it was because the golden phoenix had seen a stranger that it was behaving this way, so he drove the bird away. He then thanked the old lady and took the road to the right.

As Bao Chu started on this road, the golden phoenix flew in front of him to block his way, trying to stop him from proceeding any farther. Bao Chu brushed it away again and walked on in big strides. The more he walked, the flatter the road became: there were no flying sands, no bramble bushes, no cliffs or precipices. Bao Chu felt a little strange. After a short while, he walked into a village. The houses in this village were all large, the men all fat and strong, and the women all slender and beautiful. When they heard that he was going to look for the sun, they were so happy that they started to dance and laugh all around him. They all raised their thumbs to him and praised him as a hero and called him a brave fellow. Right away, the families in the east brought wine and the families in the west brought food. The men pulled and the women pushed. They all wanted to invite him to eat and drink.

Bao Chu started to wonder: all the other villages he had passed through were poor and tattered, all the villagers were suffering from cold and hunger. Why was it that the villagers here were all so well-to-do? While he was thinking thus in a daze, holding his wine, the golden phoenix suddenly flew to his head, and with a plop, she dropped a hemp sandal into his wine bowl. As soon as the sandal fell into the wine, it caught fire and started to burn. Bao Chu took a good look at the sandal and found that it was the same as the ones he was wearing on his feet, and was also made of hair mixed with hemp. He immediately recognized it to be the one his father had worn when he was looking for the sun. All of a sudden, he understood everything. He threw his wine bowl to the ground and gave out a tremendous shout. Suddenly, the whole village disappeared and all the villagers vanished. All he could see were so many demons, their eyes shimmering, fleeing without a trace!

After Bao Chu had frightened away the demons, he turned around and went back to the three-forked road and started out on the one to the left.

Since the demons could not kill Bao Chu, they turned into tall mountains to block his way. Bao Chu, however, ignored them and climbed over them all. The demons changed into rivers, but again Bao Chu swam across all of them. The demons had tried to freeze him in the river but failed; they had tried to entice him into the Village of Lost Souls to murder him, but again with no avail. They were extremely frightened, so they created a wind and, like a swarm of bees, flew to the foot of Gemstone Mountain to harrass Lady Wisdom. They told her that Bao Chu had been killed on a cliff, and again that Bao Chu was drowned in a river. They tried every means to sadden Lady Wisdom so that she would shed tears, causing Bao Chu to lose his strength and fail in his search for the sun. However, Lady Wisdom did not believe them. She clenched her teeth together tightly, so as not to let one teardrop fall.

Every minute of every day since he left, Lady Wisdom

hoped that her son would find the sun and come home as soon as possible. Every day she climbed to the top of the mountain with the villagers to gaze towards the east. Each time she would stack one more big rock under her feet so that she could climb higher and see farther. Thus longing and gazing, she did not know how many months and years had passed. The big rocks under her feet had already been piled into a high stone terrace, but the sky was still pitch dark.

Bao Chu continued on his journey. He could no longer remember how many mountains he had climbed or how many rivers he had crossed. One day, he climbed over a mountain which reached halfway to the sky, and he heard a splashing sound in the far distance: it turned out that he had journeyed all the way to the Eastern Sea. He came to the verge of the sea, which seemed vast and endless. Such a huge sea! Who could know where the sun was to be found? How was he to cross it? He stood there by the sea and thought hard. Suddenly he remembered the bag of soil those villagers had given him. He opened up the bag and threw the soil into the sea. A wild gale arose, and at once many islands, large and small, appeared in the sea. Bao Chu was overjoyed. He jumped into the sea and swam from island to island toward the middle of the sea. Swimming and searching, he arrived at a far distant place. He came to the deepest, deepest bottom of the sea, and there he saw a huge cave — the cave where the sun had been hidden by the demon king.

Bao Chu swam to the entrance of the cave, where he saw that the demon king and his demons were preparing to meet him in battle. He immediately started to fight with the demon king: they fought from the bottom of the sea to the top, and from the top to the bottom again. They fought so hard that the sea water was surging back and forth in raging waves. Gradually, the demon king could stand the fight no longer. Then, the golden phoenix, taking advantage of this, started to peck at his eye. The demon king screamed, he was in such pain. The golden phoenix then flew over to peck his other eye. After the demon king had lost both his eyes, he lunged wildly back and forth until he finally bumped against a rock and killed himself. When the demon king died, all the lesser demons fled and vanished without a trace.

Without even taking a breath, Bao Chu pushed the big rock away from the entrance of the cave and found the sun. With his remaining strength, he held the sun and swam towards the surface of the sea. Swimming on and on, with greatest difficulty he finally pushed the sun halfway through the sea. But at this point, Bao Chu had used up his last ounce of strength, and could not push the sun out of the sea no matter how hard he tried. At this time, the golden phoenix flew over, put her back under the sun, spread her wings and started to fly upward. Thus the whole sun emerged from the sea. As soon as the sun left the sea, it immediately rose up into the sky.

This day, Lady Wisdom and the villagers were gazing as usual from the stone terrace on top of Gemstone Mountain. Again the escaped demons came to harrass them, but all of a sudden, ten thousand golden rays shot out from the eastern horizon. The sky turned rosy and colorful. The sun rose! Right away, a long cry pierced the air over their heads, announcing that the golden phoenix had come back. Flying and fluttering about, the golden phoenix came to rest atop the mountain.

"Ah, they have found the sun!" Lady Wisdom and the villagers shouted happily together. Their cheers shook the mountains and rocked the earth. The demons surrounding Lady Wisdom were exposed to the rays of the sun and shocked by the loud happy cheers, and they all turned into stone.

From then on, the sun rose from the east and set in the west, and people again lived in a bright and happy manner.

Even today, before the sun rises every morning, a bright star begins to twinkle. This is the star that Liu Spring transformed into. People call it the "morning star." Just as the sun is rising, thousands of golden rays dart in all directions and there are rosy colors everywhere. This is because the golden phoenix, with her wings spread wide, is carrying the sun on her back.

In order to commemorate Bao Chu's achievement in finding the sun, a lovely and elegant pagoda was built on top of Gemstone Mountain. People also built a hexagonal pavilion at the place where the golden phoenix danced and fluttered about. These are the present day "Bao Chu Pagoda" and "Phoenix Pavilion." Since the stone terrace piled up by Lady Wisdom and the villagers is the spot from which the rising sun can first be seen, it is called "Rising Sun Terrace."

The Stone Censer

One year, the marvelous craftsman Lu Ban of Shandong Province came down to Hangzhou with his younger sister. They rented a two-room shop by Qiantang Gate and hung up a sign saying, "The Lu's from Shandong. We do iron, wood and stone work." As soon as they put up the sign, their threshold was almost trampled to pieces, so many people came requesting them to be their masters. Lu Ban picked and chose one hundred and eighty of the smarter and more dexterous young ones among them to be apprentices.

The craftsmanship of Lu Ban and his sister was so superb that it seemed as if they possessed a magic axe and heavenly skills. The stone dogs they chiseled could guard a house; the wooden cats they carved could catch mice. After their teaching, the one hundred and eighty apprentices all became skilled craftsmen.

One day, as Lu Ban and his sister were teaching their students, suddenly a wild gust of black wind arose and the whole sky was filled with billowing dark clouds. It happened that a black fish monster had just descended to earth to cause trouble. This black fish monster dived into the center of West Lake and made a hole some 3,600 feet deep. When this monster blew out some air from its deep hole, the whole city of Hangzhou was filled with the foul smell of fish; when it spewed out water from its hole, a wild storm rose to the north and south of the mountain. On that day, the willows snapped by the lake, the flowers withered and the waters kept rising.

Lu Ban and his sister took all their one hundred and eighty apprentices and climbed up Gemstone Mountain to take a look. When they looked down from the mountain, they saw a vast expanse of water — the whole city was immersed in smelly waters. All the men and women, young and old, were forced to flee to the mountains around West Lake. A gigantic whirlpool was turning around and around in the center of the lake. Soon, a very wide fish mouth began to rise up in the center of the whirlpool. The fish mouth rose higher and higher, until gradually a huge fish head was revealed. Then the fish head pushed upward and suddenly a puff of dark cloud rose up into the sky. Slowly the dark cloud floated over Gemstone Mountain and slowly began to descend. Soon a dark and ugly young man emerged from it.

The dark young man turned his round bulging crossed eyes and glanced at Sister Lu.

"Ha! Beautiful girl, what do you do?"

"You asked me what I do. I am a skilful craftslady!"

The dark young man scrutinized her from head to toe: "Right, right! You have bright eyes and curved eyebrows. You must be skilful in cutting silk and brocade. Come! You come with me and make me new clothes."

She shook her head.

The dark young man scrutinized her from foot to head and said, "Right, right! You have a slender body and delicate hands. You must be very skilled at embroidering dragons and phoenixes. Come! Come with me and embroider my brocade coverlets."

She shook her head.

The dark young man failed again and again to guess what she did. Finally, he thought for a moment, squinted his eyes and said, "Beautiful girl. It doesn't matter if you can't cut, sew or embroider. When you are married to me, you'll have an endless supply of delicacies from mountain and sea to eat. You may just relax and enjoy yourself!" So saying, he stretched out his hand to pull Sister Lu.

Lu Ban swung his hammer down and stopped the dark young man's hand, shouting, "You get the hell out of here!"

The dark young man still displayed a big grin and said shamefacedly, "My skin is three feet thick. I'm not afraid of your hammer! Everything will be fine if she marries me. If she doesn't, I'll raise the water and flood the hills!"

Sister Lu thought to herself that if the water was any higher, people of the whole city might lose their lives. Her eyes roamed around a few times until an idea came to her. "I can't be too hasty in marrying you. First, I'll have to ask my brother to prepare a dowry for me."

When the dark young man heard this, he was very much pleased. "My dear girl, I agree. What kind of a dowry do you want?"

"High up in the mountain, high up there is a rock. I want my brother to make a great censer out of that rock."

The dark young man was so happy when he heard this, he slapped his thigh and cried, "Great! Marvelous! Black Fish King in heaven has come to earth to establish a temple. If we have a stone censer as your dowry, we can very well use it to collect tribute."

Sister Lu pulled her brother aside and they discussed the

matter for a while.

Lu Ban then addressed the dark young man: "There's water in the east, and there's water in the west. How can we do it? First you have to take away the flood. Only then can we start to work."

The dark young man opened his wide mouth and took a deep breath. With one suck, all the water in the city flew up and poured back into his stomach.

Lu Ban pointed to a precipice on the mountain: "Look at that! What do you say we cut off half of that mountain and make it into a censer?"

"Oh good, good! Hurry, my brother-in-law! The bigger the more impressive!"

"The censer will be high, and it will be huge. It will be so heavy, how are you going to move this stone censer?"

"Now, now, now. As soon as I lift up my foot, a black wind will blow behind me. What's a little stone censer anyway! I could suck away a whole mountain if I wanted to."

After all the people who had fled to the mountain went home, Lu Ban and the others climbed to the precipice that was hanging upside down. Lu Ban swung his big hammer and landed the first blow on it. The hundred and eighty apprentices struck with their hundred and eighty hammers right after him. "Whoop!" With a thunderous roar, the precipice tumbled down. – And from then on, a sharp cliff was left on Gemstone Mountain by West Lake.

What a huge rock! If you looked at it from the side, it was white and mammoth. If you looked at it from the other side, it was mammoth and white. How could one make this into a perfectly round stone censer? Lu Ban took a good look at the hole in the center of West Lake and estimated its size. He stood in the center of the stone, holding on to a long rope, and asked his sister to hold on to the other end and run, lickety-split, around him once. Thus her footprints made a perfect circle on the rock. Lu Ban chiseled a pattern and the hundred and eighty apprentices all started to chisel according to his pattern. They chiseled day after day, and they chiseled for seven times seven, forty-nine long days all together. Then the precipice disappeared and one could see nothing but a gigantic stone incense burner. At the bottom of this perfectly round incense burner, there were three sharp legs in the shape of upside-down gourds. On the tip of each leg, there were three round penetrating holes through which the light could shine.

When the stone censer was finished, Lu Ban said to the dark young man, "Look at it! Just look at it! My sister's dowry is ready now. Please take it to the lake!"

The dark young man wanted his bride.

"No hurry, no hurry!" said Lu Ban. "You take the dowry and set it up first. Then you can send a bridal sedan chair to come and fetch her."

The dark young man was happy beyond description. He turned around and started to run downhill. The wind that he stirred up behind him indeed took the gigantic stone censer rolling right behind him. Running on and on, the dark young man transformed himself into a black fish at the center of the lake and dived into the hole. Rolling on and on, the stone censer came to the center of the lake. It slipped on the slanted side of the deep hole, and, with a "splash" it tipped over and covered the hole tightly without leaving even the slightest seam.

The black fish monster was covered under the stone censer in the deep hole and could not breathe. He tried to push up, but the stone incense burner would not even budge. He wanted to start a wind, but he had no way to turn himself around to start one. There was nothing he could do but try with all his might to dive deep, deeper down. However, the deeper he dived, the lower the stone censer sank.

Finally the black fish monster was smothered to death at the bottom of the lake. The stone censer also settled down into the mud at the bottom of the lake, with its three legs in the shape of gourds left showing above the water.

Since then, a wondrous scene was left at West Lake. On the night of the Moon Festival on the fifteenth of the eighth month, people would row to the center of the lake and light candles inside the holes of the legs of the incense burner. When the candle light shone on the lake, it was as though several moons appeared on the surface. Thus, this place has come to be called "Three Pools Mirroring the Moon."

Xing Chan

L ong, long ago, there was an Apricot Blossom Village by West Lake, and living in the village was a clever and capable girl called *Xing Chan* (Beautiful Apricot).

One early summer afternoon, when Xing Chan was seven or eight years old, she was tending a cow on the grassland in an apricot forest in front of the village. The apricots on the trees were ripe, and all the red and yellow apricots sent out puffs of fragrance. Suddenly, one of the biggest and reddest apricots fell down from the tree and landed by Xing Chan's feet.

She picked up the fallen apricot. Just as she was about to put it in her mouth, she heard a clear and ringing voice say, "Little girl, little girl! Don't bite! Let me go."

Xing Chan looked around her. It was quiet and there was nobody around at all. Who could have been talking to her? In her surprise and wonder, her fingers loosened and the apricot fell to the ground, and just then a strange thing happened. The apricot changed into a lady of such beauty rarely seen in this world, standing right in front of Xing Chan. It turned out that she was none other than the apricot fairy!

The apricot fairy pulled a bright and sparkling gold hairpin from her hair and put it in Xing Chan's hand. Then she said smilingly, "My kind and diligent little girl, take this gold hairpin from me. Sometime when you find yourself in a critical situation, you only need to knock on the gold hairpin and call for the apricot fairy three times, and I'll come to help you." After saying this, the apricot fairy turned back into the big red apricot and flew right back onto the tree.

After Xing Chan grew up, she was married to the ninth son of Master Song. After marriage, the young couple lived happily and harmoniously and her parents-in-law both liked her very much. Everything was fine in the family, except one thing: There were so many people in the family that they had too many different ideas. If one wanted to go east, another would want to go west; if one wanted something sweet, another would crave something salty. The father-in-law was an honest and straightforward person, and he had no way of controlling these nine strapping tall sons. The mother-in-law was a sweet person, so she could hardly manage all the daughters-in-law. Xing Chan, noticing that her father-in-law was so busy in charge of so many affairs, would come out subtly and drop a hint of a suggestion or two now and then. Her ideas were always right and good. If her mother-in-law forgot something, she would often think to remind her of it. Because of this, they often liked to discuss matters with her.

This, naturally, made the other eight daughters-in-law very unhappy. They felt that the parents-in-law all favored this youngest sister-in-law. As a result, they felt uneasy and started to talk in secret.

One day, it was Xing Chan's turn to cook for the family. Just as she had finished cooking a pot of rice and a pot of beancurd, the oldest sister-in-law came to the kitchen door and called her out to cut a pattern for shoes. As soon as Xing Chan went away, the second sister-in-law stealthily came in and added a few pieces of firewood to the stove and added a few more handfuls of salt to the pot of beancurd. When Xing Chan came back to the kitchen, a strong burning smell assaulted her nostrils. She opened up the rice pot to find the pot of well-cooked rice all burnt. When she tasted the beancurd, she found a strong and bitter taste. She thought about this for a while, then understood everything. She made no uproar, but set about adding a few more ladles of water into the pot of rice and made it into a pot of crispy rice soup. Then she added some more water into the pot of beancurd and mixed in some tapioca. In this way, she made a pot of thick and tender beancurd stew.

When it came time to eat, all those working in the fields came back and the children were all busying themselves setting up tables and benches. The eight sisters-in-law stood by and sent glances and smiles to each other, waiting to see the embarrassing situation of her having to serve burnt rice and bitterly salty beancurd.

At this time, Xing Chan laid out all the food on the tables. Full of smiles, she said, "It is so hot now! I've cooked some crispy rice soup for you to quench your thirst. And I'm sure you are quite tired of eating beancurd prepared in the same old way, so I just came up with a new idea and cooked it into a pot of tender beancurd stew for you to taste something different."

Her father-in-law, her mother-in-law, the oldest brother-in-law, the second brother-in-law, the nephews and nieces, and all the rest of the family joyfully consumed the food. As they ate, they complimented her, saying that the tender beancurd stew was so tasty and the crispy rice soup smelled so good and was so thirst-quenching. Soon they finished up the two whole pots of food.

After this incident, all the sisters-in-law came to admire Xing Chan from the bottom of their heart. Since they also noticed that Xing Chan was respectful towards the parents-in-law, considerate towards her husband and friendly towards everybody, they elected her to administer the family affairs, for in this way, the parents-in-law would be relieved of heavy responsibilities.

Xing Chan was not the least bit arrogant even after she took charge of the household. She always discussed matters with everybody else and managed all the work in the fields and the family affairs properly. The nine brothers concentrated on doing the work in the fields, and did not have to worry a bit about household affairs. In the house, the nine sisters-in-law spun cotton and wove cloth; they sewed clothes and made shoes; and they prepared all the meals properly. The mother-in-law only took care of the very young children; the father-in-law ran errands to town. The older children also had things to do: they herded the cows, cut grass, chopped firewood, and gathered dung for fertilizer. In this way, the family never had to worry about food or clothing. Gradually their livelihood was improved and they renovated their house.

Xing Chan was very fair in her management of the household. She would never favor one person over the other. Everyone in the family got his or her share of food or clothing. In this family, the older loved the younger, and the young respected the old. The brothers and sisters-in-law were all very friendly towards one another. Even the young children all behaved well.

Xing Chan also loved helping others. When the neighbors were short of firewood, food or tools, she would always lend these to them before they even asked. Therefore, the people in the village around them all praised and respected her. When people were teaching their daughters or daughters-in-law how to behave, they always said: "Take that Xing Chan as an example!"

This one praised Xing Chan, and that one praised her as well — everybody praised Xing Chan. Soon, even the emperor in the palace heard about her. The emperor did not believe there could really be such a capable lady as this, so he dispatched an envoy with one almond for the whole Song family to eat, wanting to see how Xing Chan would manage this challenge.

When the Songs learned of this imperial edict, the whole family was stunned. Only Xing Chan, calmly and without haste, took the almond from the envoy's hand: "Thank you for all the trouble, Your Honor. Please sit down in the living room and rest for a while. Please don't go until you have seen our family eat this almond."

Xing Chan moved some bricks over and made a stove right there and then. Then she put a big pot on the stove and heated a full pot of boiling water. She put the almond in the pot and boiled it until it dissolved. She put some brown sugar in the pot and started to divide the soup up ladle by ladle. Ah! There was just the right amount for everybody in the house to have one bowl. All the young and old in the family then had some sweet almond soup!

The envoy went back and reported the whole story to the emperor. He also added: "This Xing Chan is not only clever and capable, she is also as beautiful as a fairy!" When the emperor heard about this beauty, he forgot about everything else and ordered the envoy to take three thousand imperial guards to go and snatch Xing Chan away to his palace.

A large troop of soldiers and horses thundered up to West Lake and formed a tight circle around Master Song's house. The envoy went into the house and read out the imperial edict. The whole family started to cry. All the women and children cried and wailed, hanging onto Xing Chan's sleeves and skirt. The men all tried to talk and reason with the envoy, and there was a big commotion in the house.

Xing Chan reached out to stop the family, saying to the envoy: "Please wait outside for just a moment. Let me tidy up a bit and change clothes, then I will go with you."

Xing Chan walked into her room. She took the gold hairpin from her hair, knocked it on the table, and called the "apricot fairy" three times. Then the apricot fairy appeared, standing in front of her.

"My apricot fairy. This is a critical time for me. Please help me!"

"Fine," answered the fairy, "Let me move your whole family to the bottom of West Lake. There you'll live a peaceful life forever!"

Xing Chan nodded her head in assent.

The apricot fairy then gently waved her sleeves and a loud, wild gale arose. This wind took the whole Song family, their house, cows, sheep, farming tools and all, right to the bottom of West Lake.

The same wild gale blew the envoy and his three thousand imperial guards here and there, in every direction. When the wind had subsided and the waves calmed down, they could still see a chimney showing on the surface of the lake, but in a little while even the chimney had disappeared. In this way, the whole Song family sank down into West Lake gently and peacefully.

The neighbors often missed them and worried about them afterward. One neighbor wanted to try to find out whether they were still alive under the lake, so he shouted for Xing Chan by the lake, asking to borrow a plough. After a short while, indeed a plough came floating up on the water.

Later on, whenever people in the village were short of something, they would borrow it from the lake in the same way. When travelers from other places came to visit West Lake and became very tired from sightseeing and touring, all they had to do was tell Xing Chan about it and tables and chairs would float up right away for them to rest their feet.

Many years passed by this way. Then one day, some greedy person borrowed four chairs from Xing Chan and took them back to his own house without returning them. Perhaps this angered Xing Chan, for no one has been able to borrow anything from the lake since then.

Lady White

Lü Dongbin Sells Dumplings

It was the third day of the third month in the season of early spring. By West Lake, the willow branches were tender green and the peach blossoms gorgeous red, and there were visitors from all quarters here. Even the immortal Lü Dongbin from the Upper Eight Caves had turned himself into an old man with white hair and white beard, outfitted with a peddler's stall, and come to West Lake to join the crowd, selling soup dumplings. He set up his stall by a giant willow next to Interrupting Bridge.

When the dumplings in the pot had all floated up, he started yelling at the top of his voice: "Eat some sweet dumplings! Have some sweet dumplings! Three big ones for one copper coin, one small one for three!"

People all laughed when they heard his call. Some said to him: "Hey! Old man, your call is wrong! Switch the price of your big ones and small ones!"

Lü Dongbin ignored them and shouted as before: "Three

big dumplings for one copper, one small dumpling for three!"

Soon everyone came over and surrounded his stall. This one would take out a copper and so would that one; they all bought the big ones. In a short while, all the big dumplings in the pot had been sold.

At this time, a man aged about fifty pushed his way into the crowd carrying a small boy in his arms. When the boy saw other people eating dumplings, he also started shouting for some. But all the big ones were sold, so the man had to fish three coppers from his pocket and buy a small one for the boy. Lü Dongbin took the money. First, he ladled some boiling broth into a bowl, then picked up a small dumpling and put it in the broth. He stooped down, holding the bowl in his hands, then started to blow into it: the little dumpling jumped up onto the edge of the bowl and started rolling around the rim, around and around it rolled!

The child was immensely pleased. He was just going to pick up the dumpling and eat it when, just as though it were alive, the dumpling rushed into his mouth and slipped right down into his stomach.

After the boy had swallowed this dumpling, he did not crave anything to eat for three days and three nights. His father was very much alarmed and brought the boy to the willow tree by Interrupting Bridge to find the soup dumpling seller.

"Ha, ha!" When Lü Dongbin learned about this he laughed loudly, then took the boy and carried him up to the bridge. Before the boy knew what was happening, Lü Dongbin had picked him up by his feet and was carrying him upside down, shouting, "Come out!" The little dumpling that had been swallowed three days ago came rolling out of that little mouth in the same shape it had when it went in three days ago. It fell on the bridge and rolled down, down, down into West Lake.

Beneath Interrupting Bridge, there was a white snake that was cultivating itself to attain divinity and magic powers. The white snake had already cultivated herself for five hundred years and had acquired a certain level of divine spirit and power. She often stretched her head out to observe what was happening in the human world. Seeing that the wind was gentle and the sun warm by West Lake, and that there were so many people — male, female, old, young — in groups of all sizes, some enjoying the scenery, others just laughing and joking, some rowing boats, some planting trees, others planting flowers, still others busy making a living, the white snake began to feel extremely envious of life in the human world.

On this very day, she was emerging from the bottom of the lake, and it was just at this moment that the little dumpling rolled off the bridge. She caught it and with a "gulp" she swallowed it immediately.

The Immortal Peach Party

Bright and early one morning, a puff of white smoke rose by Interrupting Bridge and a young lady wearing soft shimmering white clothes ascended from the bottom of the lake. How beautiful she was! She looked exactly like a lotus freshly emerged from the water!

It happened that Lü Dongbin's little dumpling was a pill of immortality and when the white snake swallowed it, five hundred years of cultivation was added to her previous training. Now that she had acquired a thousand years of cultivation, she transformed herself into a human being, and gave herself the name "Lady White."

On the birthday of the Queen Mother of the West, all the immortals went to her "immortal peach party." So many of them came that they filled up the whole Cloud Piercing Hall. On this day, Lady White also attended the party to celebrate the royal birthday. This was her first time to come, and not knowing the place or anyone else there, she sat herself quietly in the very last seat.

After a little while, the fairy girls came holding the gorgeous red peaches. Everyone began to drink toasts with the birthday wine, and then the Queen Mother herself came out to greet her guests. When she saw Lady White, she looked her over from head to toe, from right to left and concluded that she just did not know this person.

She asked the old Immortal of the Southern Extremity: "Who is this lovely lady?"

The Immortal of the Southern Extremity stroked his dazzling white beard and said to Lü Dongbin laughingly: "Perhaps you should be able to explain this!"

Lü Dongbin was confused. He thought and thought, but could not understand why he should be able to explain this. When the Immortal of the Southern Extremity saw that Lü Dongbin was stumped, he broke into a loud laugh, then told the whole story that started with Lü Dongbin selling soup dumplings at West Lake. The story gave Lü Dongbin and all the other immortals a good laugh.

The story the Immortal of the Southern Extremity told made Lady White think of her old wish, and she said to herself: "I tried to cultivate myself for five hundred years under the lake and how lonely I was! I saw the good and beautiful human world up above the lake, but being a snake, I could not live among people. Now that I have swallowed the pill of immortality and been transformed into a human being, I really should give the human world a try!" She also thought of the little child who had spat out the pill; maybe she should go take a look at him too.

When the party was over, Lady White walked to the

South Gate of Heaven and saw the Immortal of the Southern Extremity. She hurried over and grabbed hold of his wide sleeve.

"Old immortal! Sir! Tell me how the child who spat out the pill is doing? I'd like to go see him."

When he heard this question, the Immortal of the Southern Extremity laughed loudly: "Do you think he is still a little boy? Your brief visit in heaven lasted eighteen years in the human world. That little boy is already a young man now!"

When Lady White heard this, her heart gave a flutter. "Then how can I find him?"

"You go down now and go look for him by West Lake. The tallest and shortest man you find there will be the one."

This said, the Immortal of the Southern Extremity stepped on a cloud and floated off.

The Tallest and Shortest Man

Lady White left the South Gate of Heaven and descended to West Lake, arriving at the Su Dongpo Causeway.

She walked along the Causeway until she came to Wave Reflecting Bridge, where she saw an old beggar with a small dark-colored snake dangling in his hand. When the dark snake saw Lady White, it wiggled both its head and tail, and tears dropped from its eyes.

Lady White took pity on it: "Dear old grandpa, what are you going to do with this snake?"

The old beggar replied: "I'm going to take its gall bladder and sell it!"

When Lady White heard this, she looked at the little dark snake again and really felt sorry for it. "Grandpa, I have some money, won't you sell it to me?"

The old beggar nodded his head in agreement.

After Lady White had bought the dark snake, she took it to the lake and put it in the water, when suddenly a puff of black smoke rose from the lake and a young girl dressed in a black shirt and black skirt walked out of the smoke.

Lady White was so happy to see her, she took the girl's hand: "Dear little girl, what is your name?"

"My name is Little Black."

"Well, Little Black, why don't you just be my companion?"

Thereupon, Little Black treated Lady White as her elder sister and they went off together.

Walking on and on, they proceeded from the inner lake to the outer lake and then back again. After every few steps, Lady White would stop and look this way and that.

Little Black had no idea what they were doing: "My sister, what are you looking for anyway?"

Lady White smiled and told her the riddle that the Immortal of the Southern Extremity had given her and asked Little Black to help solve it.

Now, this day just happened to be Tomb-sweeping Day, and the weather was very fine. There were groups of people here and there; some going up the hills to sweep tombs and others coming to the lakeside to enjoy the scenery. There were even more people by Interrupting Bridge. Lady White and Little Black threaded their way back and forth through the throngs of people, looking for the man who was tallest and shortest. However, none of the tall ones were short, and none of the short ones were the least bit tall. Yes, finding this person would be no easy task!

By noon, Lady White and Little Black had made their way back to Interrupting Bridge.

At this time, there was a small circus in action right under the giant willow tree by the bridge, and a throng of spectators were crowding around to watch.

Little Black looked around, then suddenly shouted: "Sister, it's the tallest and shortest man!"

"Where? Where is he?"

"There, look!" Little Black pointed to the giant willow tree. And there sitting in the fork of the tree, was a young man.

Lady White took a look at him: "He's not tall!"

"He is sitting there high up in the tree and people walking back and forth all have to walk under his legs. He must be the tallest person!"

"But he's not short!"

"His shadow is on the ground and whoever walks by has to step over his head. Doesn't that make him the shortest person?"

"That's right, you're right! He must be the one!" And then Lady White thought to herself: "Ah, dear old immortal! That was a tough riddle! The tallest and shortest turned out to be a young man who is neither tall nor short!"

Lady White took a good look at the young man and found that he was very handsome, with quite an honest look about him. She was both surprised and pleased. The only thing now was that he was sitting there in the tree, and she did not even know his name. How was she to make him come down from the tree? Little Black then came up with the idea of having Lady White use her magic power. In no time, dark clouds covered the sky and amidst roaring thunder a heavy rain started to fall.

The circus had to pack up and the crowd dispersed right away. The young man climbed down from the tree and ran to the shore of West Lake, where he called to a boat and told the boatman to take him to Clear Wave Gate.

Just as the boat had pulled away from the edge of the

lake and before the boatman could even set his oars straight, Lady White shouted from the shore: "Hello, grandpa boatman! Please give us a ride!"

The young man poked his head out of the cabin and saw two young ladies standing on the shore, drenched by the rain and wet as chickens in a pot of soup. He told the boatman to return to shore and let them come aboard.

As soon as they stepped on the boat, they thanked the young man.

Little Black asked him his name.

"My family name is Xu. I once met an immortal by Interrupting Bridge, and so my father called me *Xian* (Immortal)."

Lady White and Little Black glanced at each other and both nodded their heads.

Lady White then asked Xu Xian where he lived.

"Since my father died, I have been all alone. So for the time being, I'm staying with my sister and her family at Clear Wave Gate."

When Little Black heard this, she clapped her hands, laughing: "What a coincidence! My sister is just like you, with no one to rely on, wandering here and there. It seems that you are ordained by Heaven to be a pair!"

Xu Xian blushed and Lady White lowered her head.

While they were talking so happily, they heard the boatman sing this mountain folksong:

"The Moon Matchmaker's shrine is right ahead,
Lovers from afar are bound by a single thread.
Through wind and rain they cross in the same boat,
From far away they have found each other: now on
    one pillow to bed."

The Dragon-boat Festival

After Lady White and Xu Xian met on the boat on West Lake, they fell in love and were married a few days later.

Since Xu Xian was now a married man, it was no longer proper for him to stay in his sister's house. He had to start a home of his own and make a living. The young husband and wife discussed this matter and decided to move to Zhenjiang, taking Little Black with them. There, they opened an office and a pharmacy, which they called the *Baohe Tang* (Hall of Assured Harmony).

After they opened for business, Lady White would prescribe and Xu Xian would dispense the medicine. They made large pills, powdered medicine, ointments, and small pills of their own prescription. They set up a sign in front of the shop, saying, "We give medicine free to the sick who are poor." News traveled fast, and soon their Baohe Tang became well-known. Some people would come to get medicine and others to give their thanks after the medicine cured their illness. Every day, from morning till night, so many people were coming and going that they almost wore the threshold thin.

The fifth day of the fifth month was the Dragon-boat Festival. As was the custom, people hung calamus and moxa leaves above their doors to ward off evil and sprinkled realgar wine to drive away snakes and insects for the coming year. A dragon-boat race was planned to be held on the Changjiang River beneath Gold Mountain. Throngs of people were out celebrating the festival and there was much hustle and bustle everywhere.

Early that morning, Lady White called Little Black: "Today is the fifth of the fifth month, the Dragon-boat Festival. Do you remember it, Little Black?"

"Yes, I do."

"The first three quarters after noon is the hardest for us to endure. You hurry and go hide in the mountains for now!"

"What about yourself?"

"I have a thousand years of training behind me. You are not to be compared with me."

"I think it would be safer for us both to go and hide."

"If both of us leave, he will worry about us!"

Little Black realized that she was quite right: "Please take care, sister," and so saying, she jumped out of the window, turned into a puff of black smoke and shot off deep into the mountains.

As soon as Little Black had left, Xu Xian came running upstairs, shouting: "Little Black, get everything ready. Let's all go and watch the dragon-boat race."

Hearing this, Lady White answered towards the staircase: "I've asked Little Black to get me some embroidering thread. You go ahead yourself. And don't forget to take some *zongzi* (sweet rice cake wrapped in bamboo leaves) for snack!"

Xu Xian continued upstairs and came close to Lady White. "This is the first chance for us to watch the dragon-boat race since coming to Zhenjiang. You come with me!"

"I don't feel so well. You go by yourself, and come home as soon as you can."

When Xu Xian learned that she was not feeling well, he moved a small pillow onto the table and started to feel her pulse. After feeling the pulse on both the left and right wrists, he exclaimed: "You're not sick. You're fooling me!"

"I didn't say I was sick. I'm going to have a baby!"

When Xu Xian heard that he was going to be a father, he was so happy he jumped three feet high in the air. Now he didn't even care about the dragon-boat race any more, he only wanted to stay home and keep his wife company to celebrate this festive day.

At lunch time, Xu Xian called for Little Black and found that she had still not returned, so he went to the kitchen and heated up a bunch of the *zongzi* and a bottle of aged wine. Then he mixed some realgar in the wine for the holiday and took everything upstairs. He poured two cups of the realgar wine and handed one to Lady White. When she accepted the wine cup, the powerful smell of the realgar rushed straight to her head and she felt unbearably sick.

"I won't drink wine. I'll just eat a couple of the *zongzi* with you."

Xu Xian would not take no for an answer and tried to persuade her: "It's a festive day. One must have a taste, whether one can hold wine or not."

"There is realgar in the wine. I'm afraid I can't have any on account of the baby."

Xu Xian burst into laughter: "Do you take me to be ignorant of these matters? My ancestors for three generations have all been pharmacists! This realgar can drive away evil, guard the fetus and calm your mind. You should drink more of it!"

Lady White was afraid that her husband might suspect her and, relying on the fact that she had experienced one thousand years of training, she bravely drank a mouthful of the realgar wine. Unfortunately, as soon as the wine reached her stomach, it started to act up. She immediately felt her head becoming heavy as lead and she developed a splitting headache; her whole body went limp and she could no longer even sit up.

Lady White dashed to the bed that was draped with curtains. Xu Xian did not know what had happened, so he followed her. When he opened up the draped curtains to take a look, he found not even the shadow of his wife. Instead, he saw a white snake coiled on the bed. He was so frightened, he screamed and fell backward onto the floor.

The Theft of the Magic Fungus

Little Black was hiding deep in the mountains, but she worried about Lady White. Seeing that the sun had passed the meridian and sensing that the first three quarters of the afternoon had passed, she went back home in a puff of black smoke. She walked upstairs and to her great surprise, found Xu Xian lying dead in front of the bed on which Lady White was soundly asleep!

Quickly she woke her up: "Sister, wake up! Wake up! Look what has happened!"

When Lady White got up from bed and found her husband dead, she cried: "It's all my fault! I was so careless. I must have revealed my true shape and scared him to death!"

"Crying won't help. Think of a way to revive him!"

Lady White felt Xu Xian's chest and found there was still a bit of warmth left. "There is no herb or medicine in this world that could bring him back to life. I'll have to go to Mount Kunlun to steal a magic fungus!" So saying, she stamped both her feet, whereupon a patch of cloud rose under them. Riding on this patch of white cloud, she floated out of the window and off towards Mount Kunlun.

After just a moment of flight, she arrived at the top of Mount Kunlun. Now this was a supernatural mountain, full of immortal trees and immortal flowers and plants. At the top of the mountain, there were a few beautiful, purplish fungi, the magic plant that could bring the dead back to life again. Quietly, Lady White knelt down and picked one fungus, which she held in her mouth. Just as she was about to ride off on the patch of white cloud, she heard a cawing noise in the sky and saw flying towards her the white crane who was in charge of the plants. Seeing that Lady White had stolen a magic fungus, the white crane was not about to let her off easy. It spread its big wings and darted towards Lady White aiming with its straight beak. Just as the beak was about to jab at Lady White, in the nick of time, the crooked handle of a walking stick appeared from behind the crane and hooked its long neck. Lady White turned around to find a white-bearded old man standing there: it was the Immortal of the Southern Extremity.

She cried and begged him: "My venerable dear immortal! Please just give me this one magic fungus to save my husband's life!"

The old immortal stroked his white beard, and nodded his head in assent.

Lady White thanked him profusely and flew away on the patch of white cloud, carrying the magic fungus in her mouth.

She brewed the magic fungus into a liquid, then fed it to Xu Xian. After a little while he was revived; he looked at Lady White again and again. He was so frightened that he turned around and ran downstairs to hide in the accounting room.

One day, two days, three days and three nights passed and still Xu Xian did not even dare to step on the stairs.

The third night, Lady White and Little Black came down to the accounting room and asked him: "Why have you not gone upstairs for three days and three nights?"

Xu Xian hesitated, not knowing how to answer this. Then he said, "Oh, business has been so good! I've been too busy with the accounts."

Little Black could not help smiling: "What kind of accounts are you tending to, sir? Just look what you have in your hand!"

Xu Xian looked at his hand and found that in his haste he had picked up an old almanac by mistake. He knew he could not get by with lying, so he told the truth.

Lady White wrinkled her brow: "I'm nothing but an ordinary person. How could I turn into a snake? You must have made a mistake!"

Little Black interrupted: "Sir, you made no mistake, I saw it too. That day, when I came back from buying thread, I heard you shouting. When I rushed upstairs, I found that you had fainted on the floor. I saw something shining white, like a snake or a dragon fly out of the window and disappear!"

Lady White laughed: "So, that's what it was! Ah, it must have been the old dragon revealing himself. This means we'll have good luck. It coincides with our flourishing business and our baby that is to come. What a pity I fell asleep. Otherwise, I would have burnt some incense to thank him for coming and bring us good luck!"

Xu Xian noticed that they both seemed very earnest and sincere about the whole thing, and after careful consideration, he decided what they said was quite reasonable, so the clouds of suspicion dispersed in no time.

The Flooding of Gold Mountain

In the Western Heavens, there was a turtle who always hid himself under Buddha's lotus seat to listen to the recitation of sutras, and after listening for several years, he learned some magic powers. Once, when Buddha was taking a nap after his sermon, this turtle stole his Three Treasures — his gold begging bowl, cassock and black-dragon staff — and ran off to this world.

The turtle turned a somersault on the ground and transformed himself into a dark and strong monk. Believing that his magic powers were strong and that he could do anything, he named himself *Fa Hai* (The Sea of Magic

Lady White

Powers).

The monk Fa Hai took the three stolen treasures with him — the cassock on his back, the gold begging bowl in his hand and the black-dragon staff on his shoulder — and traveled from place to place. One day, he came to Gold Mountain Temple in Zhenjiang, and seeing that the waves on the `Changjiang River were strong and billowing, the mountains well-situated and majestic, he decided to take up residence in this temple. He used his black magic to assassinate the old monk in charge of the temple and made himself the head monk.

Fa Hai was bothered by the fact that not many devotees came to burn incense at the temple, so he spread an epidemic in the city of Zhenjiang to attract people's incense and money. However, the "anti-epidemic pill" and the "anti-plague powder" produced by the Baohe Tang were so effective that the epidemic was checked and did not spread. Fa Hai was so enraged by this that he disguised himself as a mendicant monk, with wooden chanting block hanging at his chest, and went searching for the source of his trouble. Every three steps, he would beat once on his chanting block, and thus he waddled his way to the Baohe Tang.

When Fa Hai reached the door of the medicine shop, he peeked inside and saw a young couple busy prescribing and dispensing medicine. He was upset at this, and inquiring in the neighborhood he discovered that the effective anti-epidemic medicine was all prescribed by Lady White. Then he took a careful look at this lady in the sheer shimmering white blouse and skirt. Aha! This was no ordinary human being! She was a transformation of a white snake! The monk Fa Hai gnashed his teeth together and sat himself quietly in front of the medicine shop, waiting and waiting until morning had turned to dusk. Just as the medicine shop was closing, he noticed that Lady White had gone upstairs, so he started to beat on his chanting block and swayed into the shop.

He put his palms together in prayer fashion: "My benefactor! How the business flourishes in your shop! Won't you please make a donation?"

Xu Xian asked him why he was seeking donations.

"On the fifteenth of the seventh month, we are going to have a deliverance meeting to mark the Ghost Festival. Please make a donation and do a good deed. Come burn some incense on that day and pray that Buddha will protect you, bring you fortune, longevity and safety all the year through."

Xu Xian thought what he said sounded good and that he spoke eloquently, so he gave the monk a string of copper coins and wrote his own name in the donation book.

Fa Hai walked to the door and turned around to remind Xu Xian: "Be sure to come on the fifteenth of the seventh month, my benefactor!"

The days passed by very quickly and soon the fifteenth of the seventh month was here. On this day, Xu Xian got up early and changed into clean clothes.

"Darling, there is a deliverance meeting at Gold Mountain Temple today. Let's go and burn some incense there together."

Lady White replied: "I am with child and it would be too much for me to climb the mountain. You go by yourself and come home as soon as you can."

So Xu Xian came to the temple by himself. As soon as he stepped inside, Fa Hai grabbed him and dragged him into a room.

"My benefactor! It's a good thing you came today. I must tell you the truth: your wife is a demon!"

This angered Xu Xian: "My wife is a perfectly normal human being. How could she be a demon? Don't talk such nonsense!"

Fa Hai pretended to smile in merciful sympathy: "I can't blame you, benefactor! You've already been enchanted by her demonic power! I saw clearly that she is a transformation of a white snake!"

This declaration reminded him of the incident during the Dragon-boat Festival, and he was stunned.

Fa Hai noticed he was in a daze.

"Don't go home any more. Make me your master, and when you are protected by the power of Buddha, you will not be harmed by her ever again!"

Xu Xian said to himself: "The love my wife has for me is deeper than the sea. Even if she were a white snake, she would never harm me. Besides, she is now carrying our child. How could I abandon her to become a monk?" With this in mind, he refused the offer.

When Fa Hai realized that Xu Xian would never agree to become his disciple, he just went ahead and locked him up. Lady White waited for Xu Xian at home. She waited and waited, but still he did not return. A day, two days, three days passed with no sign of him. On the fourth day, she could bear it no longer, so she and Little Black came by sampan to Gold Mountain Temple to look for Xu Xian.

They docked the sampan beneath the mountain and climbed up to the temple together. At the gate, they saw a young monk.

"Young master, do you know someone named Xu Xian in the temple?" Lady White asked him.

The young monk thought for a while: "Yes, there is a person by that name. My master wanted him to become a monk because his wife is a demon, but he refused. Now the master has locked him up."

Little Black was enraged at this. She pointed at the monk's nose and shouted: "Get that old bald-headed thief out here to have a word with me!"

The young monk was so terrified that he stumbled and rolled back into the temple to fetch Fa Hai.

When Fa Hai came and saw Lady White, he gave a sneering laugh: "What a brave snake demon! How dare you come to this world to enchant people and wreck my magic powers! Xu Xian has now made me his master. Surely you have heard, 'There is no limit to the sea of suffering, yet the shore is right there if you only turn around.' Compassion is at the core of this monk, so I will let you live if you just go back and train yourself for some good cause; but if you refuse to change your ways, you must not blame me for being merciless!"

Lady White suppressed the anger in her heart, and she begged with a pitiful voice: "You do your job as a monk, and I do mine in a medicine shop. We are like well water that brings no harm to the river. Why do you have to find fault with me? Please let my husband come home!"

Fa Hai was not about to reason with her. He lifted his black-dragon staff and aimed it right at Lady White's head. Lady White now had to defend herself, and Little Black also came forth to help. But the black-dragon staff fell like a mountain on her head, and since she was pregnant, she could not keep up her defense for long, so she had to retreat.

When they had retreated to the foot of the mountain, Lady White pulled a gold hairpin from her hair and waved it in the wind. It turned into a command flag embroidered with waves of water. Little Black took the flag and waved it forward three times above her head. In a wink, billowing floods surged forth and legions of shrimp soldiers and crab generals surged onto Gold Mountain.

When the floods reached the gate of Gold Mountain Temple, Fa Hai panicked. He quickly took the cassock from his back and threw it outside the gate. A golden light flashed by and the cassock changed immediately into a long dike which kept the billowing floods outside.

Each time the floods rose a foot, the dike would grow one foot higher. The floods rose ten feet, and the dike grew ten feet higher. No matter how strong the waters, they could not get over the dike.

Lady White realized that she could not defeat Fa Hai, so she asked Little Black to recall the floods and troops.

They went back to West Lake to train themselves more, waiting for an opportunity to take revenge.

The Gold Phoenix Tiara

Although Xu Xian was locked inside Gold Mountain Temple, he never would agree to become a monk, and after half a month, as soon as he found an opportunity, he escaped from the temple.

When he arrived back at the Baohe Tang medicine shop, he found that both Lady White and Little Black had left, and the house was empty. How miserable he was! But he was also afraid that the monk Fa Hai would come looking for him again, so he dared not stay in Zhenjiang. He packed up some of his belongings and went back to Hangzhou.

When he came to Interrupting Bridge, he saw that the giant willow tree was still green and flourishing. Then he recalled how he and his loving wife were separated by the monk Fa Hai, and the more he thought about it, the more painful it became until gradually tears began to trickle down his cheeks. He stamped his foot in desparation and cried: "Lady White, my Lady White! Where will I find you?"

At this very moment, Lady White and Little Black were training themselves at the bottom of West Lake, where they vaguely seemed to hear someone shouting and crying. The voice sounded quite familiar: when they listened carefully, they discovered it belonged to none other than Xu Xian. They surfaced from the bottom of the lake. They found a leaf, blew upon it, turned it into a boat, then rowed until they came to the shore to look for Xu Xian.

Husband and wife met again by Interrupting Bridge. They talked about all that had happened since they were parted, feeling both happy and sad at the same time. Talking on and on, without realizing it they both started to cry.

Little Black stood by at the side: "Now that you've found each other, what is there to cry about? Isn't it about time we found a place to stay?"

Thus, the three of them boarded the little boat and rowed to Clear Wave Gate, where they stayed at the house of Xu Xian's sister.

Time went by very quickly, and soon New Year had passed. At the time of the Lantern Festival on the fifteenth of the first month, Lady White gave birth to a fair and healthy little boy. Xu Xian was so happy he never stopped smiling. He smiled at everybody.

On the day their child was one month old, the family was to throw a soup-and-cake party, according to custom, to celebrate his first full month of life. Xu Xian's sister and Little Black were busy tending to all the affairs inside and outside the house. Lady White got up early to do her make-up and get ready. Xu Xian was standing by his wife, watching: he saw her red and tender cheeks, her dark and shining hair. She was even more beautiful than before. Watching and thinking, he suddenly realized that she was to present the child to the older generation of relatives and friends to receive their blessing today. What a pity they had left all their good jewelry at Zhenjiang ....

Just then he heard a hawker shouting in the alley: "Gold tiara! Gold phoenix tiara for sale!"

When he heard this, Xu Xian ran with giant steps out into the alley to look for the hawker. When he saw the sparkling gold tiara, made with all kinds of jewels, he fell in love with it and bought it.

He took it into the room: "Darling, I bought a gold phoenix tiara for you. Try it on and see if it fits."

As soon as Lady White saw the beautiful and shining gold tiara, she liked it and told Xu Xian to put it on her freshly combed hairdo. But once he had placed the tiara on her head, it would not come off again, no matter what. Gradually it grew tighter and tighter, until finally Lady White felt such a splitting headache that gold stars sparkled before her eyes, and she fainted and fell to the floor.

This unexpected disaster stunned Xu Xian. He stamped his feet wildly and ran out into the alley to look for the hawker. When he reached the gate, he found not the hawker but the monk Fa Hai, standing there with his black-dragon staff blocking the way: the hawker had been none other than Fa Hai in disguise. Ever since Xu Xian fled his temple, he had been traveling far and wide in search of him. Today he had learned that they were celebrating their son's first full month, so he changed his gold begging bowl into a tiara and himself into the hawker, and come to their door. Now, as Fa Hai saw Xu Xian come flying to the gate with a pale and frightened look on his face, he knew that his trick had worked.

He rushed forward with a sneer: "My benefactor! You did not heed my kind words and good reasoning. Today I have come to collect the demon!" So saying, he walked toward their room in big strides. Xu Xian tried to stop him, but in vain.

Fa Hai blew on the gold phoenix tiara and it turned back into his gold begging bowl. The begging bowl then produced ten thousand gold rays which tightly surrounded and covered up Lady White.

Little Black rushed up to fight with Fa Hai, but Lady White shouted from inside the golden rays: "Run, Little Black! Run! Quick! Go and train yourself some more, then come back to take revenge for me!"

Little Black knew that she could do nothing to Fa Hai now, so she fled in a puff of black smoke.

Xu Xian grabbed Fa Hai and held him with all his might. Then, from inside the golden rays, Lady White told him: "Darling, take care, take care! You must look after our child!"

Xu Xian was just an ordinary human being, and could do nothing to the monk Fa Hai. He could only pick up their child from the bed and show him to Lady White for one last look.

Tears stained Lady White's face. Slowly, her body began to shrink under the golden rays. At last she turned into a white snake, which Fa Hai collected into his gold begging bowl and left.

After Fa Hai had obtained the white snake, he built the *Leifeng* (Thunder Peak) Pagoda on top of Thunder Peak in front of Pure Compassion Monastery on Mount Nanping. He placed his gold begging bowl beneath the pagoda and imprisoned the white snake under it. Finally he settled himself into Pure Compassion Monastery to guard the pagoda.

The Fall of Leifeng Pagoda

Little Black remained deep in the mountains to train herself. There she stayed and trained herself for years — no one knows how many — until she felt that her powers were very strong. Then she rushed back to Hangzhou to look for Fa Hai in order to avenge Lady White.

At this time, Fa Hai was still guarding Leifeng Pagoda. When Little Black found him at Pure Compassion Monastery, they engaged in a fierce battle at the foot of Mount Nanping. There they fought for three days and three nights. Little Black became increasingly fierce in battle, while the monk Fa Hai was gasping for breath. When they had fought to the foot of Leifeng Pagoda, Little Black swung her sword and Leifeng Pagoda collapsed with a thunderous crash. Lady White jumped out of the pagoda and joined Little Black in fighting Fa Hai. The monk was already beginning to tire, and now that Lady White had joined in the battle, he could defend himself no longer. Now he could only fight as he retreated, trying to flee whenever possible. In his haste, he retreated to the shore of West Lake. He slipped and, with a splash! he fell straight into the lake.

Seeing that Fa Hai had fallen into West Lake, Lady White pulled her gold hairpin from her hair, waved it in the air, and turned it into a command flag. Little Black took the flag and waved it backward three times above her head, and all the water in West Lake immediately dried up, baring the bottom of the lake to the sky. Fa Hai tried to hide everywhere, but could not find a safe place for himself. Finally, he noticed that there was a crack just under the crab's belly button, so he dived right into that crack. The crab drew his belly button in and the monk Fa Hai was locked inside. Now he could never get out again!

Originally, the crab used to walk straight ahead like other creatures. However, since the monk Fa Hai carried on in such a devious and unruly manner, the crab could no longer walk straight, and it began to walk sideways!

Even as we eat crabs today, when we open up the shell, we still find the bald monk hiding inside!

The Foul Qin Hui

Beside West Lake there is a tomb called the Yue Tomb in which the famous general Yue Fei (1103-1141) was buried. There were four cast iron statues kneeling in front of the tomb, among them those of Qin Hui (1090-1155) — the traitor who caused Yue Fei's death, and Qin Hui's wife.

It was said that during the Ming Dynasty (1368-1644) a new governor came to Hangzhou to take up office. This person was also named Qin, and was said to have been a descendent of Qin Hui. Not long after this new governor took office he went to visit West Lake, accompanied by several followers. When he came to the Yue Tomb and saw his own ancestors kneeling there, he hurriedly covered his face with his sleeves and backed away from the place.

When he returned to the yamen, he was so upset that he could neither sat nor stand comfortably, so he called his advisor in to discuss the matter of removing those two statues.

His advisor thoughtfully stroked his beard for a while: "If we tried to remove them publicly, the local people probably wouldn't allow it. It might even cause an incident. I think it would be better to send some people to remove the statues in the dark of night and throw them into West Lake. Once they have sunk into such a big lake, even if water were drawn, no one would ever find them."

The Governor said: "What a marvelous idea! Perfect!"

He sent people to throw the iron statues into the lake that very night.

A very strange thing happened at dawn the next day: the water in West Lake suddenly began to smell foul. The putrid smell rushed to the very sky and made the passers-by feel dizzy and faint. Everyone felt like throwing up.

Then someone discovered that two statues were missing in front of the Yue Tomb, and started yelling: "Come and see! Two statues are missing! Someone must have thrown them into the lake. Otherwise, how could the water have become putrid?"

When the townspeople learned about the disappearance of the statues at the Yue Tomb, they all rushed to report to the yamen. They demanded that the culprit be caught and punished.

The Governor was still in bed when he heard people yelling and shouting outside. He got up and asked for the reason, and his attendent told him. The Governor felt guilty, so he made it known that he was sick.

But people would not leave, and more and more of them came to the yamen, almost breaking the stone lions that stood in front of the gate. The Governor, afraid that something might happen, came out to meet the towns-people in spite of himself.

"This ... this must be some silly rumor. You must not believe such a thing!"

"You decide whether it is a rumor or not after you actually have seen it," was the reply. They all rushed forward to surround him and pull him to West Lake. The

Governor could do nothing but step into his eight-man sedan chair and head towards West Lake.

Indeed, a foul, putrid odor sailed through the door of the sedan chair when they were still a few miles from the lake. Fortunately, the Governor had not had time to eat breakfast, for if he had, it would have come rushing out again.

When the sedan chair arrived at the lake and the Governor took a look from behind the curtains, he saw literally hundreds of people all around. His heart pounded intensely as he stepped slowly out of the door.

He pretended to cough a few times: "It is not unusual for lake water to smell once in a while. You must not make such a big thing out of nothing! I personally think this has nothing to do with the iron statues!"

Someone shouted from within the crowd: "Who are you? Are you related to Qin Hui or something? How dare you try to be partial to Qin Hui?"

The Governor did not know how to answer this for a moment. He tried to calm and comfort himself: "Don't worry now," he thought. "The statues have already sunk into the lake. Who could find them?" Thus thinking, he became braver and proudly shouted: "Now don't you make trouble! If someone can actually retrieve the iron statues from the bottom of the lake, I will gladly resign and accept punishment!"

Just as the Governor had closed his lips after this speech, the ink-black lake water suddenly became so clear that everyone could see the bottom of the lake. From the bottom of the lake, a pair of iron statues floated up and drifted towards the Governor, as if someone were supporting them from beneath. The Governor was so frightened that his face became like wax paper and, leaving the crowd behind, he dashed into the sedan chair, shouting "Hurry up! Run!"

When the sedan chair arrived at the yamen, its roof was full of holes made by hurled rocks. Even the Governor's head was decorated with three big walnut-sized bumps. Forgetting his official hat and abandoning his official boots, he fled from Hangzhou that very night.

When the iron statues had floated to the edge of the lake, the townspeople pulled them up and put them back where they used to be, kneeling in front of the Yue Tomb.

The Little Yellow Dragon

The fog was dense and thick at Purple Cloud Cave, where an old yellow dragon dwelled. This yellow dragon was no longer young, and he had done many evil deeds in his day. Drowsily and sleepy-eyed, he slept in the cave from morning till night, with no desire even to move a muscle.

There was also a little yellow dragon in the cave. The little dragon had no parents of his own, and had been the old yellow dragon's slave ever since childhood. The old yellow dragon was afraid that the little dragon might escape, so he would not allow him to go even one step out of the cave. Even when he slept, he would keep one claw on the little yellow dragon's neck.

Once, the old yellow dragon was sleeping deeply and soundly, ah, so very soundly. The little yellow dragon gingerly and quietly slipped out from under the old dragon's claw. He came to the opening of the cave and the minute he swished his tail, the purple clouds covering the entrance dispersed. He came out of the cave and saw the green mountains and blue waters, the tender green crops and gorgeous red flowers. He was so overjoyed that he turned a somersault on the ground and he immediately transformed himself into a fine young man. Little yellow dragon saw that his naked body was still covered with dragon scales on the back, so he pulled two pieces of the purple clouds over, blew on them and turned them into a set of purple clothes, which he put on.

When the little yellow dragon walked down the hill, he ran into a young cowherd sitting there crying.

"My little brother, why are you crying?" he asked the cowherd.

The cowherd wiped his tears with the back of his hands. "I lost a cow that belongs to the rich Master Two and he has asked me to give him back a cow. I don't have a cow to give!"

"So what if you don't have a cow. Why should you cry?"

"He said that if I do not come up with a cow in three days, he will club me to death."

Hearing this, the little yellow dragon blinked his eyes and thought for a moment: "Little brother, don't cry. I will give the cow back for you!"

The cowherd scratched his head and went with the little dragon.

The little yellow dragon went into a forest with the cowherd and there they saw an old man weeping under a tree.

"Dear uncle, why are you crying?"

The old man cleared his throat: "I owe the rich Master Two two bushels of grain in rent and he has just pressed me to pay him. I don't have the grain!"

"So what if you don't have the grain. Why should you cry?"

"He said that if I don't come up with the rent in three

days, he will put me in prison!"

Hearing this, the little yellow dragon blinked his eyes and thought for a moment: "Don't worry, I will pay the rent for you!"

The old man straightened his back and went along with the little yellow dragon.

The little yellow dragon walked along the cobble road with the cowherd and the old man until they came upon an old lady crying in front of a house.

"Dear granny, why are you crying?"

The old lady cleaned her nose: "I owe the rich Master Two some money and he has just pressed me to pay him back. I don't have the money!"

"So what if you don't have the money. Why should you cry?"

"He said that if I don't pay him back in three days, he will wreck my house!"

Hearing this, the little yellow dragon blinked his eyes and thought for a moment: "Please don't cry. I will pay the money back for you!"

The old lady dusted off her garment and went along with the little yellow dragon.

After walking for some time, they finally arrived at the gate of rich Master Two's home.

The old lady noticed that the little dragon was empty handed, so she asked: "What the rich Master Two wants is money. You didn't bring any money. How can you pay my debt?"

The old man also saw that the little dragon was empty handed, and asked: "What the rich Master Two wants is grain. You didn't bring any grain. How can you pay him back for me?"

The young cowherd also noticed that the little yellow dragon was empty handed, so he asked: "What the rich Master Two wants is a cow. You did not bring a cow. How can you pay him back for me?"

The little yellow dragon answered, "Dear uncle, dear granny, little brother, let me ask you this: what does he like most?"

They all answered together: "What he likes most is gold! money!"

The little yellow dragon slapped his ankle: "That's right! That's right! And I have gold. We'll pay gold for the rent, gold for the debt, and gold for the cow." So saying, he discreetly reached into his garment. With a jerk, he ripped off a gold scale from his back. Then with another jerk, he ripped off another gold scale. He went on ripping the scales from his body. The old saying goes, "A dragon fears the ripping off of the scales." Now since the little dragon was tearing off his own scales, you can imagine how painful it was for him. He clenched his teeth together and bore the pain. At last he had peeled all the golden scales from his back and divided them among the old man, the old lady and the cowherd.

They all went into the rich Master Two's house. When Master Two saw them, he shouted: "Hey you, cowherd, give me my cow! And you, old man, pay me my rent! And you, old woman, return my money!"

The old man gave him gold scales to pay his rent; the old lady gave him gold scales to pay her debt; and the cowherd gave him gold scales for the lost cow.

Holding a pile of gold scales in his hands, the rich Master Two wrinkled his brow and murmured, "These flakes are really gold. And they are so shiny. What a pity they are loose and without dignity!"

At this point, the little yellow dragon stepped in: "Master

Two, if you make a big fire, you can melt them into a soft jelly, then you can make it into one huge ingot of gold so big you can't even move it out of your door!"

When the rich Master Two heard this, he was so pleased that his face was covered with bumps from laughter, his eyes became a slit and his smiles reached his ears.

When the little yellow dragon came out of the rich man's gate, he blinked his eyes, thought for a moment and said to the old man: "Why don't I take you as my own dear father?" The old man stroked his beard and agreed with pleasure.

Then the dragon said to the old lady: "Why don't I take you as my very own mother?" The old lady smiled and agreed with pleasure.

Then the little yellow dragon turned around and addressed the cowherd: "Little brother, why don't you take me as your big brother!"

The young cowherd was so happy with this that he jumped up and wrapped his arms tightly around the little yellow dragon's neck.

From that time on, the old man, the old lady, the cowherd and the little yellow dragon became one family. The dragon learned how to plant crops with the old man, but he would only work in the dry fields and not in the water paddies. He helped the old lady do the chores, but he only chopped wood and was unwilling to fetch water. The little dragon went to tend the cow with the cowherd, but he only walked on bridges and did not want to step on the wet sand or into the river. The others all felt that this was rather strange, but they did not quite understand why.

After the rich Master Two had received all the gold scales, he was in a daze for three whole days. On the fourth day, he told his servants to build a big blazing fire in the house in order to melt the gold scales into a huge ingot. He also prepared a feast and invited all his rich and powerful relatives and friends to observe this event and allow him to show off his wealth.

Unexpectedly, as soon as the gold scales entered the fire, the flames leaped thirty-three feet high with a swoosh. The beam of the house immediately caught fire and in the twinkling of an eye, the rich man's house was burnt down flat onto the ground. Now it turns out that the little yellow dragon was a fire dragon, and that the scales from his body were none other than the "fire dragon scales." Once these scales caught fire, there was no way that the flames could be extinguished.

Once the rich man's house caught fire, the air was full of dense smoke. Clouds upon clouds of smoke rushed into the sky. The smoke and flames floated up and up to the hills and came into Purple Cloud Cave. Thus the smoke wafted into the old yellow dragon's nose. His nose started to feel itchy and he sneezed. Now a sneeze was nothing to him, but his sneeze blew smoke and flames right out of the cave with a swoosh and burnt up all trees, crops and houses within one mile of the cave.

With this sneeze, the old yellow dragon woke up. He sniffed and smelled about, and concluded something was wrong. He instinctively started to call for the little yellow dragon but the little dragon was nowhere to be seen in the dark cave. The old dragon was enraged and rushed out of the cave to look for him.

Flying through the air, the old yellow dragon searched to the west and to the east. He flew over one hill after another until finally he came to the burning house. After a careful look, he shouted: "Oh, my goodness, my goodness! This house belongs to the rich Master Two! He always sacrifices three different kinds of animals to me on festive days and in return I have always avoided his house when spitting fire on others. How could it have started burning on its own today?" He sniffed carefully some more and shouted, "This smells like burning fire dragon scales. That little yellow dragon must have done this! I'm going to find him and throttle him to death!"

The old dragon flew back and forth in the air but he could not find the little yellow dragon no matter how he tried. He was so angry that he began breathing very hard. As he breathed, flames darted out from his mouth and nose and plunged the city of Hangzhou and its immediate environs into a sea of flames.

The grain was burnt, and nothing was left to eat. Clothes were burnt, and there was nothing left to wear. Houses were burnt, leaving no place to live. How could the people endure a life like this? The little dragon knew this must have been the evil doing of the old yellow dragon. He blinked his eyes for a whole morning and thought hard for a whole afternoon.

At last, he became brave and said to the villagers: "My dear villagers! The fire dragon has been too wicked. He has done too much evil. We must unite and subdue him!"

"But the fire dragon is a deity, how can we subdue him?"

"Earth overcomes water. Water overcomes fire. The fire dragon fears water. First let's all go and get water from West Lake, then I'll take you to find the fire dragon!"

This idea worked like a wild wind to raise the interest of villagers in three hundred and sixty villages in all directions when they learned of it. That very evening, people started to bring water from West Lake by every means available to them. West Lake was drawn dry in no time at all. The villagers followed closely after the little yellow dragon as the crowd stumbled their way to Purple Cloud Cave.

At this time, the old yellow dragon was asleep after having become very tired from all the day's flying, and he had not the faintest idea what was going on outside. As the crowd climbed up the hill, they saw nothing but a huge patch of dense fog, and they searched back and forth with no success in finding the entrance to the cave. Then the little dragon waved his arms in the fog and the purple clouds covering the cave dispersed. The crowd rushed to the cave and started to pour, sprinkle and splash water into Purple Cloud Cave. Soon, water had filled the cave and the old yellow dragon was soaked and drowned shortly after.

With the crowd busily and frantically splashing water into the cave, everybody was splashed, and even the little yellow dragon was sprinkled with drops of water. Soon he felt rather faint and his body went limp. As the old man, the old lady and the cowherd ran over to support him, they saw horns come out of his head and his hands and feet turn into claws. The little yellow dragon had revealed his true form. Then he tumbled down and died at the foot of the hill. Only then did they realize that this young man was actually the transformation of a fire dragon.

Now that the old yellow dragon had died, the fire in the city died out too. But the little dragon had sacrificed his life for the people, and this saddened them very much. People from all the three hundred and sixty villages gathered together to bury the little yellow dragon on the slope of the hill.

Their tears fell as they dug the grave, but they kept on shoveling the soil and the little yellow dragon was buried. Soon a large mound was piled up and hundreds and thousands of tear drops were falling down. They penetrated the thick soil and flowed straight into the little yellow dragon's heart. His heart was soon full, and as it could no longer contain all the tear drops, they started to flow out from his mouth. Gradually, a crack appeared in the grave mound and a waterfall poured down from it. The clear waters splashed down all through the year without end.

Later on, to commemorate the little yellow dragon, a statue of a dragon's head was erected at the source of the waterfall and the water then flowed from the dragon's mouth. The spot where the little dragon was buried then came to be known as "Yellow Dragon Cave."

Jade Spring

In Clear Ripple Temple north of *Xiangu* Hill (Fairy Maiden Hill), there is a rectangular pool called "Jade Spring" whose water is pure and crystal clear.

How did this crystal clear spring water come to be?

There is a story to it.

Many, many years ago, there was a bottomless ditch at the Qiantang River mouth called "Heaven-made Stream." There lived in this ditch a crude dragon. This dragon could make waves and billows in rivers and seas, and fly upon the clouds and ride the fog. He was very strong and could do many things, but he was coarse and did not know the first thing about worldly affairs. All day long he would dive in the rivers and jump out of the seas, playing and having a good time with all the fish and shrimp.

One day, an official boat, escorting two lighters, was passing through the Qiantang River mouth. There was shouting and the crash of gongs coming from the official boat, which was just brimming with dignity. However, nothing but the sound of crying and howling came from the two lighters. When the dragon noticed this, he felt it was very strange. After much inquiry, he learned that there was an emperor in this world and that he had many officials under him. Those who were crying were the common people who had been caught by the emperor's officials to perform labor in the capital. When the dragon learned this, he became very indignant. He swished up his tail and, with a big splash, a billowy wave overturned the official boat, and the people on the two lighters were thus saved. The dragon thought to himself: "It is true that I have overturned the official boat. But the emperor is still in the capital city! He is such a wicked emperor that I really should do away with him and exchange him for a better one." Therefore, he leaped up from the Heaven-made Stream and, riding on some dark clouds, flew towards the capital city.

The emperor was drinking wine and having fun with his subjects and ladies in the royal court at this time. The palace ladies were playing various kinds of musical instruments, singing songs and dancing. How happy they were! Then, all of a sudden, the weather changed and the sky clouded over. A wild gale almost snapped the trees; a torrential rain began pouring down with no letup. In the midst of all this, the dragon angrily broke in, riding on dark clouds. This frightened the three thousand imperial guards so much that they darted in all directions, covering their heads. The emperor was so stunned that his eyes and mouth remained wide open. In all this commotion, there was one brave imperial guard who pulled his crossbow to the fullest and shot a pellet into the dragon's right eye. The dragon was in such pain that he gave a thunderous yell, turned around and, with a "swoosh," he toppled one corner of the palace with his tail, then flew away.

When he came back to the Heaven-made Stream at the mouth of the Qiantang River, he became more and more angry thinking about it. He gritted his teeth and vowed to take revenge.

An old monk who was highly skilled in healing was living in Clear Ripple Temple at the time. When the dragon found out about this monk, he transformed himself into a crude and dark man, and came to the monk to be healed.

The monk, seeing his rather odd appearance, was very suspicious. "*Aiya*! What happened to this eye?"

The dragon lied and said that a flying rock had hit it when he was chipping stone.

When the monk removed the thing in his eye with pliers and found it to be a pellet, he threw it on the floor: "Clearly this is a crossbow pellet. Why did you say it was a piece of flying rock? Who are you? If you don't tell me the truth, I will not treat you!"

When the dragon realized that the old monk was really angry, he was afraid that he would not take care of his wound, and in the end he honestly told him what had happened and how he had received a crossbow shot. He concluded his story by saying, "Once you heal my eye, I will go back to take revenge!"

When the old monk heard this, he was shocked. He thought to himself that his temple and monastery were built by none other than the emperor and that he was supported by the emperor. Now this thing wanted to go and harm his benefactor. This would never do! So he thought of a plan and, with artificial smiles, he said to the dragon: "It won't be hard for me to cure your eye, but how will you thank me?"

"If you can cure my eye, I'll give you whatever rare treasures you might request!"

"I don't want any rare treasures. Water is what we lack in this monastery. Why don't you first bore an opening for a spring that we could use?"

The dragon had no idea that this was a trick, so he agreed happily.

The old monk chose a spot, and the dragon bored into the ground head first. Clear spring water then gurgled forth from the hole where the dragon had drilled himself into the ground. He bored deeper and deeper, and the spring water gurgled up with even more force. Soon the water accumulated into a big pool. At this point, the old monk rushed over to the statue of Buddha, brought the elegant stone pagoda from there and put it right in the middle of the spring opening. The dragon was covered under the ground.

The dragon had been tricked by the old monk and he was never able to come out of the ground again. The water from the spring that he bored was as clear and pure as jade, so people called it "Jade Spring." There were two other pools near Jade Spring. One of them was called "Pearl Spring" and the other, "Spring of Clear Skies and Joyful Rain." It is said that the dragon's head is beneath Pearl Spring, so when the ground there is stamped upon, the dragon will wake up. When he exhales, many small bubbles come gurgling up to the surface of the water. The dragon's tail is coiled under Spring of Clear Skies and Joyful Rain, and that's why it is always misty over the spring, even on a clear and bright day.

Fly-in Peak

It is said that on Mount Emei in Sichuan Province, there was once a mountain peak that could fly, and it would indeed fly here and there from time to time. Each time the peak would fly and land somewhere, it would crash down upon many houses and kill many people.

At that time, there lived in Soul's Retreat Monastery at West Lake a monk who was rather crazy and who did not obey the prohibition against touching wine and meat, so people all called him Mad Monk.

One day, Mad Monk learned that the strange flying peak was going to fly and land on the village in front of the monastery at noon time. He was worried that many people would be killed when the mountain peak landed, so he got up at dawn and ran into the village. He went from house to house, telling the people: "A mountain will fly to the village this noon. Hurry up and move! If you don't move fast it will be too late."

When an old man heard him, he shook his head: "Mad Monk, you're playing jokes again! Mountains are too heavy. Who has ever seen a mountain that could fly?"

When the master of a house heard him, he sighed: "We are only poor tenant farmers. Where are we going to move to?"

When a young man heard him, he made a "hmmph" sound through his nose: "Baloney! If the mountain comes down, we'll carry it on our shoulders. We're not afraid!"

Little children all followed him, laughing and gesturing, joining in the fun.

Mad Monk went in and out of house after house. He had finally given his warning to all of the more than one hundred households. He talked until his lips were bleeding and his mouth was parched, but not one person in the whole village believed what he was saying. And naturally, not a single family was making preparations to move away.

The sun was rising higher and higher and noontime would be here at any moment.

Mad Monk was so panic-stricken that he was walking in circles. Just then, he suddenly heard the sound of trumpets blaring, so he quickly rushed in the direction of the sound. He arrived and took a look. What on earth! It was a marriage ceremony! The bride and groom were just in the midst of kowtowing to heaven and earth! The place was filled with a joyous atmosphere, with people walking here and there. What a bustling scene! Mad Monk scratched his head and thought for a moment. Then suddenly he pushed his way through the crowd and ran right into the ceremonial hall. Without a word of explanation, he lifted the bride up onto his shoulder, dashed to the gate and started to run away from the village.

The groom hadn't even had a chance to take away the red silk veil and see his bride's face yet, and here she was being carried away already. She, having absolutely no idea what was happening, was screaming at the top of her lungs. Mad Monk was running away with the bride. Good heavens!

Some villagers took up crossbars from their doors; others picked up poles; some were swinging their hoes; others raised up their rakes; all of them chasing with all their might, chasing and shouting: "Catch that crazy monk!" "Block his way! Don't let him go!"

This startled the whole village. Whether they were friends, relatives or strangers, all the men and women, old and young, the whole village joined in the chase.

Only the rich landlord and his family at the east end of the village did not stir. They stood in front of their gate and watched this spectacle.

"A monk is running away with a bride. What do you know! Hee hee!"

Mad Monk, with the bride on his back, was running away for all he was worth. He was so fast! All the villagers chased him for more than three miles and still no one could catch him. Then, just as the sun reached the meridian, he stopped running and stood still. He put the bride down, and sat on the ground to fan himself. The villagers caught up, and were just going to grab him and beat him up, when all of a sudden it turned pitch dark, so dark that they could not even see their own fingers. A wild wind rose with a "swoosh," and suddenly, a loud crash shook them so much that they all fell down on the ground. By the time they had scrambled up, the wild wind had stopped, the clouds had dispersed, the sun was shining again, and they saw that a mountain peak had just fallen on their village. Now they all understood: Mad Monk had run away with the bride in order to save their lives.

But now that the whole village was under the mountain, they had nowhere to turn. Some were in such a desperate state that they started to howl, beating their chests and stamping their feet.

Mad Monk said, "What are you crying about? Don't you

realize that the landlord in the village was crushed under the mountain? From now on you can till your own land. Soon you should be able to build your own house again!"

The villagers were pleased to hear this. Just as they were going to go away, Mad Monk spoke again: "Don't go. Don't go yet. Listen to me. Since this mountain peak was able to fly here, it certainly may fly away, and when that happens, it will harm many people again. If we carve five hundred statues of Arhats on it, this mountain can be held down and never be able to fly away again. Shall we do it?"

When the villagers heard this, they all agreed that this was a good idea, and started the job immediately. Some hammered and others chiseled. "Bang! Bang!" They worked all night until they finished carving five hundred statues of Arhats. Now the whole mountain was covered with niches and statues of Buddhist Arhats. The only drawback was that they had made the bodies but did not have time to chisel the eyes and eyebrows on them.

Mad Monk said, "I can do it! Leave that to me!"

Without the use of a hammer or a chisel, using only his very long finger nails, he scratched over the Arhats' faces. In half a day, he had put eyes and eyebrows on all the statues.

From then on, this little mountain peak could no longer fly away and it has stayed in front of Soul's Retreat Monastery ever since. Because it flew over from some place else, it was then called "Fly-in Peak ."

Monkey Calling Cave

Tomb-sweeping Day, when the willows are green and the peach blossoms red, is the time when the scenery at West Lake is at its very best. One such day, there were people everywhere, strolling around, enjoying the scenery. In front of Soul's Retreat Monastery, there was a lot of hustle and bustle and commotion.

The Governor of Hangzhou also came out to enjoy himself on this day. With gongs banging and yamen runners announcing his arrival, he came to Soul's Retreat Monastery. He noticed that there was a large crowd gathered at the foot of Fly-in Peak, so he told his runners to clear a path through the crowd so that he could get closer and see what was going on there. Aha! It was an old monk playing chess with a golden-haired monkey. Now the Governor was known for his intense interest in chess. Those who would flatter him all praised his skills to the very skies, saying that he was the peerless national master of chess. As soon as he saw the chess and chess board, his hands started to itch for a game. He kicked the monkey away and sat down to challenge the old monk, intending to show off his skills before the crowd.

The old monk understood that all officials had a great sense of pride, so he humbled himself and intentionally fouled up a few moves to lose the game. When the Governor won the game, he was so happy that he stood up and laughed loudly with his head held high. In fact, he even said a few uncomplimentary things about the monk.

The monk thought to himself, "I have been kind enough to save you your pride, but in return you have tried to insult me!" Then he also started to laugh. When the Governor saw that he was laughing, he said: "Are you mad? You've just lost the game, and you're laughing!"

"Your Honor! Among strong hands, there is always one stronger than the others. I have a teacher who is above me!"

"Where is your teacher? Would he dare to come out to play me a game?" The Governor immediately asked.

The monk pointed towards the hill: "There, that's my teacher!"

The Governor raised his head to find the golden-haired monkey that he had kicked away. The monkey, at this time, was swinging from branch to branch on the trees of Fly-in Peak.

"Bah! I thought it was someone important. It turns out to be nothing but a hairy monkey! Why don't you call him over here to have a game with me!"

The old monk clapped his hands facing the hill and the monkey came jumping over to the old monk. Eyes gleaming, the monkey looked at the Governor. The monk made a gesture and the monkey sat down on the seat and started to play chess with the Governor.

The Governor was no match for the monkey! After only a few moves, the Governor had already lost the game. His face flushed from ear to ear. He looked at the crowd, and found that everyone was smiling, biting their lips together.

Fly-in Peak

He cleared his throat: "What a wily hairy monkey! This one doesn't count. We'll play again. Another game!"

Again the Governor lost. He was in such a panic that his face turned red, and then turned pale. Large drops of sweat started to trickle down from his forehead. When the crowd saw the dignified Governor lose to a mere hairy monkey, they all started to jeer and laugh. Now that the Governor had lost face in front of this crowd of people, he became extremely angry. His face clouded over and he stood up all of a sudden. He threw the chess board to the ground, and shouted, "Take this animal and give him a beating!"

The yamen runners all rushed up like a swarm of bees. When the old monk saw that the whole thing had gone amiss, he clapped his hands over the monkey's head, and shouted "Be gone!" Then the people heard a "swoosh" as the monkey shot up to the peak.

The yamen runners all ran after him. The monkey, however, swung and jumped back and forth from this tree to that. He was here at one moment and there at another, more agile than a squirrel. The yamen runners chased after him for a long time and were all out of breath, but still they could not catch him. The Governor was so angry that he trembled all over, and shouted loudly: "Set fire to the hill! Burn the whole hill!"

When the yamen runners had made their torches ready, they heard the monkey jump off a tree with a plop and, with a long shout, dive into a cave by the tree. The yamen runners immediately followed him into the cave, but when they got inside, they discovered there was no opening leading anywhere. There were only the rock walls, and yet the monkey had disappeared. They went and reported the situation to the Governor, but he would not believe them. He had to go in to inspect it himself. When he got in, he seemed to see the monkey hiding there against the rock wall. He rushed forward to catch it. However, he rushed too fast and ran smack into the rock wall and crushed his nose. There was nothing he could do but to walk out of the cave, covering his nose with his hands; and he returned to his office in dejection.

Nobody saw the golden-haired monkey again after he went into hiding in the cave. He would only come out when the old monk clapped his hands in front of the cave and called for him.

Later on, the old monk died and the monkey in the cave never came out again. Since the old monk used to call for the monkey in front of the stone cave, people have always called it "Monkey Calling Cave."

Stone Man Ridge

A long, long time ago, Hangzhou was nothing but a dry stretch of ocean beach. There was not a river or a stream within a radius of several dozen miles. People who lived here had to go to a far away place to fetch water with buckets everyday. They worried day and night for the lack of water, with the result that they never lived a happy day's life.

Some of the older generation knew that in the back part of Soul's Retreat Mountain there was a clear spring which was blocked by an extremely thick stone wall and could not flow out. For years and years, many young men had gone to the mountain and tried to drill into the stone wall, but they all had failed. Gradually, only a very few survivors knew about this.

In the back village, there was a young man named Waterboy who was orphaned at a very young age and had been brought up by his grandfather. Ever since he was six years old, he had been fetching water with his grandfather, and this had lasted for fifteen years now.

On this particular day, it was Waterboy's twentieth

birthday. His grandfather made a big pot of birthday noodles and the two of them spent a very happy day together. That night, grandfather called Waterboy to him and told him all about the clear spring.

Waterboy was very happy to learn about this. He tightened up his belt, rolled up his sleeves and gathered all his friends together. They planned to go and drill through the stone wall, so that the clear spring could flow into their village. When his grandpa saw that Waterboy had such high aspirations, tears started to flow down his cheeks. He spent the whole night getting food ready in order to send them to the mountain the next day.

On the next day, ten young men, equipped with hammers and chisels, were ready to go to the mountain. Before they left, grandpa told the young people: "When you work on the stone wall, you'll have to do it in one burst, without stopping. If you stop, the wall will revert to its original shape and you only will have wasted your energy. Also, when the stone wall is finally penetrated, a stream of liquid stone will rush out first. If it gets on your body, it will turn you into stone. Be sure to remember all this!"

Waterboy and his friends promised to be careful and left for the mountain.

As soon as they arrived at the mountain they started chiseling the stone wall. They hammered and chiseled and chiseled and hammered. They worked from the Tomb-sweeping Day in the third month to the Dragon-boat Festival in the fifth. Their chisels were worn short and their hands were covered with bloody blisters, but still they had not penetrated the stone wall.

Four of the young men finally said: "Perhaps your grandpa didn't remember right. How could there be any clear spring here! Better to go back and draw water with buckets as usual!" So saying, they left.

The remaining six young men kept on working from the Dragon-boat Festival in the fifth month to the Mid-autumn Festival in the eighth, but they still had not penetrated the stone wall. Their chisels were much shorter and their hands were covered with calluses.

Two other young men said, "Do it in one breath indeed! Who knows how long this is going to take? We really should go home and see how things are now!" So saying, they left too.

Autumn had passed and winter was here. The snow on the mountain was half the height of a man. The northwest wind howled and pierced into people like daggers. The four remaining young men worked · without stopping for a breath. They chiseled on and on until the following spring. By the time the azaleas were gorgeously red, they had made a deep, deep dent into the stone wall.

On the third day of the third month, Waterboy suddenly heard the gurgling sound of water on the other side of the stone wall. He pressed his ears to the stone wall to listen, then shouted out in amazement: "Ah, the spring! It's the sound of spring water!"

His companions also jumped up with joy.

Waterboy turned around and told them: "You'd better leave. The liquid stone will be coming out any minute now!"

Knowing that the spring water was about to come out, none of them could bear to leave.

Seeing that none wanted to leave, Waterboy cried out in panic: "If you don't leave, I'll stop chiseling!"

When they heard this, they were afraid that he really might stop working; and if he stopped, they would have wasted all their time and energy, so they all scattered away.

At this point, Waterboy chiseled the last stroke. There was a thunderous roar, and the liquid stone dashed out and turned Waterboy into a stone man thirty feet tall!

Afterwards, a stream of clear water came gurgling down through the mountain valley, flowed past the village and accumulated in the marshland by the beach. The marshland was then filled to the brim — and this became what is now West Lake.

From then on, there has been no worry for lack of water in this area.

That mountain that Waterboy chiseled through later became known as "Stone Man Ridge."

Laurel Peak

One Mid-autumn Festival evening, during the reign of the Tang Emperor Minghuang (713-756), a bright full moon hung in the sky, illuminating the world below.

In the middle of the night, the monk *Deming* (Virtue and Intelligence) who was in charge of the stove in Soul's Retreat Monastery got up to make some rice porridge when he heard a string of drip-drop, drip-drop sounds. He thought it was strange, and when he looked out of the window, he only saw the moon, shining bright. Where had the rain drops come from? He opened the door and went out to see, and when he looked up, he saw millions of little pearl-like objects falling down from the moon and showering onto the mountain peak by the monastery. He stood there and watched until they stopped falling, then he climbed up the peak to look for them. Whenever he found one, he would pick it up, and in this way he went on looking and picking. The little pearl-like objects were all round and solid, about the size of soybeans, and they were of many colors. They were beautiful! He went on picking and picking from mid-night until early morning, when he had picked up a big bagful of them.

That morning, Monk Deming brought all those pearl-like things to show them to the old monk *Zhiyi* (Wisdom First), and asked him what they might be.

Monk Zhiyi looked at them carefully and replied, "There is a large laurel tree and a crude man called Wu Gang in the Moon Palace. Wu Gang chops at the laurel tree all year round but it always grows back again. Sometimes, if he happens to chop too hard, the laurel seeds may fall off. Perhaps these are laurel seeds from the tree in the Moon Palace!"

Monk Deming was happy to hear this: "Master, let's plant these seeds so that people can view the laurel trees and enjoy the fragrance of laurel flowers like in the Moon Palace."

Therefore, they planted all those colorful pearl-like things on the mountain slopes in front of and behind the monastery. In ten days, these seeds had actually sprouted. In one month, the tender shoots had grown into small trees over one foot tall and they had sent out tender green leaves.

How fast these laurel trees from the Moon Palace had grown! They grew one foot each month and more than ten feet a year. By the time of Mid-autumn Festival the next year, they all had grown into big tall trees. Each tree was densely laden with small blossoms of orange, pure white, dark red and every other color. Monk Deming then named the different trees according to the colors of their flowers, calling them the golden laurel, silver laurel, cinnabar laurel, and so on. From that time, there have been laurels of all varieties surrounding West Lake.

Today there is a mountain peak by Soul's Retreat Monastery called "Laurel Peak" and it is said that this is the place where the laurel seeds fell from the Moon Palace.

A Thread of Sky

Years ago, never mind how many, there once lived in Zhuji a young man named Stone Child, who was both intelligent and strong. He was not only a good hand in the fields, he was also an outstanding stone mason. Every day, he took his hammer and chisel and gathered all the youth of the village to chisel the rocks on the mountain. Spring, summer, autumn and winter, rain, shine or snow, they never missed a day. Chiseling and hammering on and on, they gradually made the rocks on the mountain by the village lovely and attractive, adding to the beauty of the natural scenery.

In the village where Stone Child lived, there was a girl called Sister Flower, who was beautiful as a peony in bloom. She was clever and skilful, and her embroidery was excellent; no one could match the quality of her work. Every day, Sister Flower embroidered by the window with the other girls of the village. Embroidering on and on, they stitched pretty flowers onto the brocade, then fashioned it into beautiful clothes, and when they put them on they were lovely to behold.

Sister Flower could also sing. Whenever she sang, flowers would blossom, birds would dance in the air and every male and female, young and old in the village would be happy and laughing. If Stone Child were chiseling rocks on the mountain and happened to hear Sister Flower's song, he would work even harder.

Stone Child was in love with Sister Flower and Sister Flower loved Stone Child. They had a common wish: they wanted to wait until Stone Child had carved all the rocks on the mountain and Sister Flower had embroidered all the flowers of all the four seasons before they married. All the villagers were fond of Stone Child and Sister Flower, saying that they were a natural-born pair.

The day they were looking forward to finally came! It was Mid-autumn Festival, and Stone Child had finished carving the last rock on the mountain and Sister Flower had used up her last strand of silk thread. Together they ran to the small stream outside the village. Sister Flower undid her braids and let the clear spring water wash through her long hair. The stream started to dance in whirls and to laugh, "gurgle, gurgle," on and on. When the peach tree by the stream saw the beautiful Sister Flower, it sent out one particularly gorgeous peach blossom from the top of the tree. Stone Child climbed up the tree, picked the blossom, and put it on Sister Flower's very first combed-up hairdo. The moon shone in the sky. The stars were winking their eyes. The fairy maidens in heaven were peeking down. Everyone was envious of this couple down in the human world!

Thunder God, standing up on the clouds, also saw that Stone Child and Sister Flower were so happy and so close to each other. The more he watched the more jealous he became. Bitterly he thought to himself: "How could there be anyone in the human world happier than I? I won't stand for this! A beautiful girl like that should belong to me!" Thereupon, he gave his face a wipe and transformed himself into a stout dark-faced chap and descended to earth.

After Sister Flower made herself up, she and Stone Child went back to the village. The villagers whisked them up the most beautiful of mountain tops where they had built them a new house. Males and females, young and old, all spent a joyous night on the mountain. They did not begin to scatter and go home until it was almost dawn.

When the guests had all left and Stone Child and Sister Flower were just about to go back to their house, suddenly the moon disappeared and dark clouds hung over their house. They heard a fearful noise rolling in from afar. Thunder God himself appeared on the mountain top.

He tugged at Sister Flower, with a nasty smile on his face: "My beauty, come to heaven with me!"

Sister Flower was so scared and angry that she reached out and slapped him twice on the face. Stone Child rushed over and knocked him far away with his elbow. Now that Thunder God had been insulted, he would not let things go. He turned his eyeballs around and around, and two streaks of lightning flashed; he opened his mouth and thunder-claps rolled out. He flapped his sleeves and a wild storm arose. The lightning dazzled them, the peeling thunder deafened them, the wild gale blew them off their feet, and the downpour left them unable to raise their heads. Sister Flower and Stone Child clung to each other tightly and would not let go for anything.

Thunder God chopped down between them with his hand and a streak of blue lightning flashed by and the mountain top split in two. Thunder God then blew upon the half on which Sister Flower was standing and it began to fly away. Stone Child smartly leaped with all his might and clung onto a tree vine on her half of the mountain top. On and on they flew, faster and faster. Stone Child heard the wind swishing by his ears and gradually he felt faint and his eyes blurred. His two hands soon turned into wings and he could no longer cling to the vine. He bit onto the vine with his teeth and held onto it tightly, but his mouth became longer and longer, and sharper, and harder. Finally, her half of the mountain flew to the sky over Hangzhou. With a loud crash, it fell on the ground and Stone Child fainted.

When Stone Child woke up, he found himself transformed into a bird and he was filled with sorrow. Then, faintly, he heard a song. What a familiar voice! He spread his wings and flew to the mountain top in search of the voice. The carvings on the mountain were done under his leadership; the trees were planted under his guidance. Then he recognized the mountain top as the half that had flown from his own village. He pressed his ears close to the rock to listen and the song became clearer. No rock wall, no matter how thick, could cut off Sister Flower's song! She must be under this half of a mountain top! Stone Child found a spot and started to peck at the rock. He pecked at it for a whole day, and then for another. He pecked and pecked until sparks flew up from the rock.

As Sister Flower was singing, she suddenly heard the faint sound of pecking. She held her breath and listened. Yes! The noise became clearer and clearer. It must be Stone Child chiseling the rock. She was overjoyed! She pulled out a silver pin from her hairdo and started to dig at the top of the cave where the noise was coming from. She was going to save Stone Child some effort and penetrate the rock more quickly. In this way, Stone Child pecked from the top, and Sister Flower dug from inside the cave. Stone Child's beak was broken and Sister Flower's hairpin was worn short. No one knows how much time passed before one day, Stone Child pecked at a silver hairpin. The rock was penetrated! A thread of warm sunshine shot into the dark cave. Stone Child flew into the cave through the thin filament of an opening and circled around Sister Flower three times. Sister Flower then also changed into a beautiful bird and the two of them flew into the sky towards the sun.

Flying on and on, Stone Child and Sister Flower penetrated the blue sky, darted through the white clouds and flew all the way into heaven. They found Thunder God and darted towards him with their wings flapping. "Peck! Peck!" They attacked Thunder God's bronze-bell-like eyeballs and blinded him. From then on, Thunder God was sightless and could only roar in heaven, but he would never again dare to come down to this earth and make trouble.

Even today, there is a mountain outside Zhuji City called "Half Mountain." The other half which was flown away is the "Fly-in Peak" situated in front of Soul's Retreat Monastery in Hangzhou. There is a little opening on top of Fly-in Peak called "A Thread of Sky." This, then, is the place through which Stone Child saved Sister Flower.

Emperor Kangxi Inscribes a Plaque

When Emperor Kangxi (reigned 1662-1722) took a trip to the south, he included Hangzhou on his itinerary. He visited all the West Lake area, sightseeing, composing poems, inscribing characters for plaques and tablets, truly playing the role of a carefree and debonair emperor.

One day, he wanted to visit Soul's Retreat Monastery.

When the old monk in charge learned of this news, he was both surprised and flattered. He quickly sounded the bells and drums, summoning together all the more than three hundred monks who stayed there. They all donned new cassocks and, sandalwood incense on their heads, tapping their chanting blocks and chanting prayers of "Namah Amitabha," they all hastened to follow the old monk to Stone Lotus Pavilion a mile away to meet the Emperor.

In the company of the old monk, the Emperor visited the monastery from front to back and inspected all the hills. Emperor Kangxi noticed that the place was brimming with tall mountains and clear springs, dense green trees covering the mountains and gorgeous red flowers carpeting the ground. What a superb spot! Finally, he was so pleased that he ordered a feast set up in the monastery.

When the Emperor had a feast set up, it was really an occasion! There were people playing wind instruments and people playing strings, while others were singing songs. For the moment, this pure land of the Buddhist monastery was transformed into the Emperor's dwelling! The Emperor, one hand stroking his goatee, the other holding a goblet, guzzled wine and intoned poems.

The old monk had long heard that Emperor Kangxi loved to intone poems and inscribe characters for others. Now, seeing that the Emperor was in quite a good mood, he went over to discuss the matter with a local official attending to the Emperor: "Your Honor! I should like to ask His Majesty to write the name of this monastery for a plaque. Might this be done?"

The Governor of Hangzhou answered: "Excellent, excellent! If His Majesty writes something for your place, my entire territory will be honored!"

The County Magistrate of Qiantang also added: "The Emperor is just now riding high on the wine. I think if you ask him right this minute, he will certainly agree."

The old monk now felt assured and, telling himself to be brave, he walked over to the Emperor, knelt down and kowtowed: "Your Majesty! For the sake of the Great Buddha of Soul's Retreat Monastery, please inscribe a plaque for us so that we may share your glory!"

This request touched the Emperor's tenderest spot. He nodded his head. He picked up the writing brush and, with a few strokes, he wrote a tilting *yu* (雨 rain) graph. Now, what he had written down was no more than one third of the first character *ling* (靈 soul) of the three characters in the name of this monastery. Since he was already quite tipsy and his hand was a little shaky and a bit too hasty, what he had written already covered up more than half of the space assigned for the character *ling*! Now there was less than half of the space left and two-thirds of the character to go! There was no way for him to put them all in properly. If he were to give up and use a fresh piece of paper, he would lose face completely. One hand holding the writing brush and the other tugging his goatee, he could not think of a thing to do. Knowing that the Emperor had gotten himself into a fix, none of the officials standing by dared to say a thing. They could only stand there panic-stricken.

Fortunately a Grand Scholar named Gao Jiangcun, of the National Hanlin Academy, finally thought of a way out. He first scribbled the characters *yun lin* ["cloud forest," the character *yun* (雲 cloud) contains *yu* in it] on his own palm. Then, pretending to grind some more ink for the Emperor, he leaned over close and secretly opened his palm in front of him. When Emperor Kangxi saw these characters, he exclaimed to himself: "*Aiya*! These two characters have really saved me!" And before he knew it, he was already half sobered up. He lifted the writing brush and hastily wrote down the characters *yun lin chan si* (Cloud Forest Zen Monastery). Then he raised his arm and cast the writing brush aside.

The old monk came closer to take a look. This isn't right! Why did His Majesty write these characters?

Having not sensed the awkward situation, he stuttered: "Our ... our place is called 'Soul's Retreat Monastery *(ling yin si)*' and not 'Cloud Forest Monastery *(yun lin si)*.' Hasn't Your Majesty made a mistake?"

Hearing this, the Emperor looked at the monk with wide eyes and shouted: "Silence!"

The monk naturally did not dare to say another word, so he stood by in a very respectful manner.

Emperor Kangxi Inscribes a Plaque

Emperor Kangxi then turned around and asked the officials: "This place has clouds in the sky and forests on the ground. Tell me, isn't it right to call it 'Cloud Forest Monastery'?"

"Yes, yes! You're right! Your Majesty is most sagacious and intelligent!"

......

All the attendant officials vied with each other to agree with him. The Emperor was so pleased that he burst out in laughter. Then he ordered that his characters be engraved on a plaque and hung up in the monastery.

The Emperor only had to say a word, and all the officials started to scramble. They ordered that the old plaque in the monastery be taken down and that engravers and carvers be summoned to engrave the words the Emperor had inscribed onto red wood. They made the background of the plaque gold and the characters ebony black. The rim of the plaque was decorated with two dragons playing with a pearl. It was put above the gate of the monastery as soon as it was finished.

From that time on, Soul's Retreat Monastery has been blessed with the false name "Cloud Forest Zen Monastery" on its plaque. However, the people of Hangzhou would not go along with this. Although the plaque which says "Cloud Forest Zen Monastery" has been hanging there for three hundred years, they still call the monastery by its old name "Soul's Retreat Monastery."

Monk Censure Teases Emperor Qianlong

The real reason that Emperor Qianlong (reigned 1736-1795) went to visit the south was not merely to enjoy its mountains and seas. It was because there were rumors that people in the south might rebel, so he used this as an excuse to investigate things in the south, hoping to find out whether there was any foundation to the rumor.

At this time, a monk called Censure was living in Pure Compassion Monastery on Mount Nanping at Hangzhou. This monk did not care very much about chanting the sutras or sitting in meditation. On the contrary, he only loved to discuss important matters of state. Whenever he felt like criticizing or censuring anyone, he never hesitated to do so, and he never worried that this habit might get him into trouble. However, his criticisms were usually correct and when he censured someone, he did so in a most interesting way, so the common folk all liked to be on close terms with him.

When Emperor Qianlong came to Hangzhou and heard about this monk, his brow wrinkled into a knot. He thought: "This monk has given himself such a strange name.

He must be a loyal subject from the previous dynasty who has withdrawn into the mountains rather than behave as a good citizen. I must go and find out what it is that he censures." Thereupon, he changed into the blue clothing of a commoner. Holding a folding fan with patterns traced in gold, the Emperor disguised himself as a student and waddled all the way to the monastery where he asked to meet with Monk Censure.

Monk Censure came out.

As soon as he came out, the Emperor asked: "Might this be the master Monk Censure?"

"That's right. I am Monk Censure and Monk Censure is me."

Emperor Qianlong continued: "Did my master become a monk when he was a child or did he become a monk midway in life?"

"Me? I became a monk midway in my life, but why do you ask me this?"

The Emperor could not answer. With a glance, he noticed that the monk was wearing a cassock covered with hundreds of patches, so he asked: "I've heard that you are a virtuous and honorable high monk. Why are you wearing shreds as tattered as these?"

Monk Censure smiled and replied: "I also wore a lot of silk and brocade in my youth! Later they were torn to pieces by dogs so I became a monk and started wearing this tattered hempen cassock! However, although what I wear is tattered, my heart inside is pure. I am not like those high officials who wear splendid clothes on the outside while doing sordid deeds in the dark."

The Emperor had been dealt a secret blow but he could not let his anger show. He thought to himself bitterly: "This Monk Censure! He's just like his reputation. I must find some fault with him so I can have him severely punished."

While thinking these wicked thoughts, the Emperor was all smiles as he asked the monk to show him the monastery.

As they entered the mountain gate of the monastery, Emperor Qianlong saw someone splitting bamboo for weaving incense baskets. Glancing to one side, the Emperor picked up a little sliver of the split bamboo, turned the green side upward and asked the monk: "My master, what do you call this?"

"This is called bamboo skin."

The Emperor turned the bamboo over and showed the white side to Monk Censure: "Then, Old Master, what do you call this?"

"This, we call the bamboo meat."

Emperor Qianlong wrinkled his brow and laughed reluctantly: "Such interesting names!"

Monk Censure avoided the real issue and said with a laugh: "Well, now that the ways of the world have changed, we must also change our terms!"

Emperor Qianlong did not get the intended response so he could only remain quiet.

Now as it happened, this was the time of the notorious literary inquisition and the court was looking for excuses to execute critics. If Monk Censure had answered the two questions with the usual terms, calling one side the "thin green lath (*mie qing*)" and the other side the "thin yellow lath (*mie huang*),"their pronunciation would have sounded like "destroy the Qing (dynasty)" and "destroy the Huang (Emperor)." Then of course the Emperor could have seized upon this to have him beheaded. The reason Emperor Qianlong had asked him these questions was that he intended for the monk to dig his own grave.

Emperor Qianlong went to the *Daxiong* Main Hall to pay his respects to Buddha and then to the Hall of Arhats to view the Buddhist statues. At last he came to the *Xiangji*

Kitchen, which was the kitchen of the monastery. The Emperor looked around and saw two baskets full of bean sprouts by the stove. Just at this very moment, a puppy walked by and, lifting his hind leg, urinated right on the bean sprouts.

Emperor Qianlong took all this in quietly and asked: "Old Master, are bean sprouts considered to be clean things?"

"Bean sprouts are born and raised in water. Naturally they are clean!"

"Hmm!" said the Emperor. "How can you say they are clean when there is dog urine on them?"

The monk burst out laughing: "It is said that what you cannot see is clean and that what you do not hear is true. If having seen it you pretended that you hadn't, wouldn't it be clean? How can you take such a trifle so seriously! There are people, for example, who are criticized by everyone in the whole country, yet they just pretend not to have heard it. They can still brag shamelessly, calling themselves sages!"

Emperor Qianlong was enraged at hearing this, yet he could not show his anger for fear of revealing himself. He wanted to find some other way to trick the monk but he could think of nothing at all. Just when he was in a fix, he heard a peddler outside shouting: "Tea eggs! Have some tea eggs!" On hearing this, Emperor Qianlong excused himself by saying that he felt hungry and wanted to buy some tea eggs. Taking advantage of this opportunity, he slipped dejectedly through the back door.

Eight-trigram Plot

When you climb half way up Jade Emperor's Hill to Purple Source Cave and look down, you can see a plot of land which is in the shape of an eight-trigram. This octagonal Eight-trigram Plot is neatly divided into eight patches of land, each of which grows a different kind of crop. These eight different crops show their eight different colors during all four seasons. In the center of all these separate plots is a round mound, in the form of a *Taiji* Chart ☯ representing the *yin* and the *yang* elements.

It is said that this Eight-trigram Plot once composed the "Imperial Farmland," whose crops were used for sacrifice to the imperial ancestors, and was opened up during the Southern Song Dynasty (1127-1279).

In the year 1127 A.D., the good-for-nothing Emperor lost his capital city Bianliang and fled to Hangzhou with a large troop of royal relatives, friends, and civil and military officials. When they saw how Hangzhou excelled in scenic beauty, they decided to settle down there and erected palace buildings and imperial gardens at the foot of Phoenix Mountain, and here they carried on their lavish life of drinking, eating and generally enjoying themselves.

The people of Hangzhou, seeing that their Emperor was so incompetent and extravagant, became greatly dissatisfied with him and began to express their dissatisfaction in the alleys and on the streets. Word of this eventually reached the Emperor's ears and, fearing that the people might rebel against him, he panicked and summoned all his civil and military officials to discuss the matter. They discussed and deliberated at length, but could think of no way to deal with the problem.

Finally, a civil official came up with an idea: "Your Majesty! The gossiping and rumoring among the people have started simply because they resent the fact that life in your court is so much more comfortable than theirs. If Your Majesty were to open up a plot of field, saying that you will till it yourself, people would admire you with all their heart and stop criticizing you."

The Emperor liked the idea, so he issued an Imperial Edict right away, proclaiming: "Inasmuch as We deeply feel the hardship of the folk, We shall open up a plot of land and till it personally, so as to share in the toil of the people ...."

A few days later, indeed a plot of the land was opened up beneath Jade Emperor's Hill. Eight neat stakes were set up and eight thick pillars were erected. A cowhide curtain was set up around the pillars — for the ordinary people were not allowed to peek when the Emperor was tilling the land there.

Some days later, the curtain was removed. There were eight individual plots inside planted with rice, wheat, sorghum, millet, etc., eight kinds of crops in all. In the center of these eight plots was a round earthen mound.

Once the people learned that the Emperor was tilling the land just as they did, they were satisfied and the rumoring gradually died down.

During the season of weeding and fertilizing, the Emperor was again to leave the palace to "personally till the Imperial Farmland." The cowhide curtain was once more set up around the pillars. Imperial guards were stationed within a circumference of three miles, and no one was allowed to go near the site.

At that time, there happened to be an old farmer who simply did not believe the Emperor would till the land himself, so this time he got up in the middle of the night and quietly slipped by the imperial guards in the dark. He stumbled and fell every two or three steps until finally he had climbed up Jade Emperor's Hill and hid himself in Purple Source Cave.

He waited and waited. Finally, day dawned and the sun rose. The old farmer looked down the hill and saw that the common folk had all started to work in their fields. However, there was not a soul inside the cowhide curtain. Not until the sun had climbed to the height of three bamboo poles did some people come out of the palace and into the tent. The old man opened his eyes wide to watch. Aha! There were only some eunuchs weeding the fields inside the curtains! The Emperor and his palace ladies were sitting there on the earthen mound, drinking and enjoying themselves!

The old man repressed his anger and, with much difficulty, waited until dark. Then he stealthily slipped back down the hill. The next day, he told some people what he had seen from the hill. This news passed from one to ten, and from ten to a hundred people, until soon everyone in town had heard about it.

When the Emperor learned that his ruse had been discovered, he never went back to "personally till the Imperial Farmland" again.

Nevertheless, this Eight-trigram Plot has been preserved to this day.

Phoenix Mountain

Phoenix Mountain

L ong, long ago, a brother and sister lived at the foot of a
mountain south of West Lake. The brother was called
Spring Lad and his sister was Autumn Lass. When their
parents died, they were left with about half an acre of
leased land and a run-down hut. They would get up before
dawn and not rest until midnight every day hoping that if
they worked hard on the land, they might get a little more
harvest. However, when the grain ripened in the autumn,
the landlord would come to collect the rent, and leave them
not even enough to live on. There was nothing they could
do but try to survive on soup and thin rice porridge each
day.

One New Year's Eve, it was very snowy and windy. In the
house of the wealthy landlord, the tables were laden with
cooked meat, fish, chicken and ducks, while there was only
one small cup of rice left in the house of the brother and
sister. Autumn Lass made it into a bowl of thin rice
porridge for her brother to eat.

Spring Lad said: "I'm not hungry. Why don't you drink
it?"

"I'm not hungry either. You have it!"

They yielded back and forth but neither would take it.

At this time, flakes of snow as large as goose-down were flying and the north wind was howling fearfully. Through this wind and snow, an old lady came to beg for food. Her hair was partly white and her clothes were tattered.

Leaning on a cane, she stumbled with every step she took. As she stumbled, she moaned: "Oh the wind-filled skies! Oh the snow-covered ground! Oh kind-hearted people, please pity this old woman!" Her hoarse cry drifted into the run-down hut and brother and sister heard it clearly.

"Listen, brother! What a sad cry." said Autumn Lass.

"Let's invite her in."

Spring Lad quickly opened the door and helped the stranger into the hut. Autumn Lass quickly brushed off the snow and Spring Lad gave her the bowl of thin rice porridge to eat.

The old lady stayed overnight with them. Next day the snow stopped and as it was clear and bright outside, she wanted to leave. Before she left, however, she brought out a piece of white silk and offered it to Autumn Lass: "Dear girl, embroider this piece of white silk with your own skilful hands. Good fortune awaits those who are kind and diligent!" When Autumn Lass looked at the silk, she saw the faintest trace of a phoenix.

Thus, Autumn Lass set about embroidering this piece of white silk night and day. She embroidered the head of the phoenix with red silk thread, the eyes with black thread, the wings with golden thread and the tail with five different colors. On and on she embroidered, and now and then she accidentally pricked her fingers, with the result that her blood made stains on the white silk. She embroidered a fiery red sun and rosy clouds to disguise the stains. She embroidered from spring solstice to winter solstice until finally she finished the whole phoenix.

What a beautiful picture of the phoenix! The head was raised towards the fiery red sun, as though alive. The brother and sister hung it up in the hut. The more they looked at it, the happier they became and the more they grew to care for it.

Then one night, something strange happened. Autumn Lass woke up to discover that the room was lit up by a bright golden light. She took a careful look and saw that the phoenix had come down from the picture. She woke up her brother and they both watched carefully. They saw the bird walk around the room once, then go back into the picture, at which time the golden light also disappeared.

Next morning when Autumn Lass got up to sweep the floor, she found a gold phoenix egg. They sold the gold egg and used the money to buy a few acres of land and a cow.

As the saying goes, "Good news travels a thousand miles"; the news of the picture of the phoenix traveled like the wind to the ears of the County Magistrate.

He thought to himself: "A phoenix in a picture that can lay golden eggs — this is truly a rare treasure. I must get it into my own hands!"

He had Spring Lad brought to him: "I admire you and want to do something nice for you. Tell you what: I'll give you three hundred ounces of silver for your phoenix picture."

"My sister embroidered that picture with much pain and care. I'm not going to sell it!"

The Magistrate pulled a straight face and rapped his gavel on the desk: "It is quite clear that this treasure belongs to the Emperor! How could any pauper have made such a precious picture!"

Without listening to any explanation, he found Spring

Lad guilty of the crime of "stealing a national treasure" and had him put in prison. At the same time, he ordered his runners to snatch the picture of the phoenix from Spring Lad's house.

The Magistrate was beside himself with joy, and he burst out laughing when the picture came into his own hands.

That very night, he sat in his comfortable armchair and waited for the phoenix to lay a gold egg. At midnight, the phoenix suddenly gave out blinding rays of light and the whole room turned a golden hue. Just as expected, the phoenix came down out of the picture. The Magistrate, thinking that the bird was going to lay a gold egg, quickly stooped down to look. Before he knew it, however, the bird was dashing towards him fiercely and started pecking at him with all its might. The Magistrate was in such pain that he rolled on the floor, yelling: "Help! Somebody! Help!"

When the yamen runners rushed in, the phoenix had already flapped its wings and flown out of the window towards the mountain. When they helped the Magistrate up, they found that his face was covered with blood and his left eye was blinded.

In spite of what happened, the greedy desire of the County Magistrate would not subside. He thought: "If that girl could embroider one phoenix picture, she must be able to do a second one!"

He ordered Autumn Lass to be brought in and told her that if she could embroider another phoenix, he would release Spring Lad. To save her brother, Autumn Lass agreed.

She brought back that piece of white silk from the Magistrate's place and started to embroider it again stitch by stitch. This went on for three months, until she finally finished embroidering a splendid phoenix. However, she did not embroider the eyes. She told the Magistrate that only after her brother was released would she put eyes on the phoenix.

The County Magistrate had Spring Lad released, and when Autumn Lass saw her brother, she set about finishing the eyes.

As soon as the eyes were completed, the phoenix spread its wings, came down, took Spring Lad and Autumn Lass upon its back and flew away disappearing into the mountain top.

Afterward, people named this mountain "Phoenix Mountain."

Six Harmonies Tries to Fill the River

It was said that the Dragon King lived in the Qiantang River. He was very quick-tempered and this often caused the tides to rise and fall at irregular times. The fields by the river bank were often flooded and people lived in fear from day to day.

At that time, there lived beside the river a fisherman, his wife and their son, Six Harmonies. When Six Harmonies was five years old, his father was drowned in the river after his boat capsized during a fishing trip.

Without the boat there was no longer a way to fish, so the times became extremely hard for Six Harmonies and his mother. Mother and son could only use two bamboo poles, each with a small round net tied to the end, and run bare-foot into the rising waters to catch the fish riding in with the tide. This was very dangerous business, for if they were not quick in running away, they would be pulled out by the tide. But mother and son had to risk their lives this way in order to survive.

One day just as they were fishing, Six Harmonies noticed that the tide was coming in extremely fast and fierce this time. He sensed danger, and started to run away for all he was worth, pulling his mother by the hand. But, it was already too late. A wave struck and took his mother away in its swirling retreat.

After losing his mother, Six Harmonies was left with nobody to rely upon and became lonelier still. He was so sad and so angry that, eyes full of tears, he started to bring rocks of all sizes down from the hill and throw them into the river with all his might. He swore to fill the whole Qiantang River with rocks, so that the tide could never again rush in in an unruly manner, bringing harm to the people.

While throwing the rocks, he cursed constantly: "Hateful tide! Damned Dragon King! I'll bring down the whole mountain and fill up your Qiantang River!"

Holes appeared in the roof, doors and windows of the Dragon King's Crystal Palace from the rocks thrown by Six Harmonies. The rocks piled up on the steps of the Crystal Palace and the entrance was almost blocked. When the Dragon King heard Six Harmonies' curses, he went to the door of the Crystal Palace to take a look, but one of the rocks hit his head and knocked one of his horns askew. A large bump rose on the back of his head and made him cry in pain.

Six Harmonies stayed by the river, weeping, cursing and throwing rocks. One day, two days .... He kept this up for a total of seven times seven — forty-nine days.

On the eighteenth of the eighth month, he suddenly heard the sound of a thunderous roar coming from afar. The tide came surging on. On the breaker of the tide there stood a fierce looking crab general leading a whole troop of C-shaped shrimp soldiers. Behind them, under a yellow silk umbrella, was the Dragon King. Soon, the Dragon King arrived in front of Six Harmonies.

"Hey, boy, little boy! Stop crying. Stop cursing. Don't throw any more rocks. I'll give you gold, silver, jewels, anything you want."

"Dragon King! Listen to me. I don't want your gold, silver or jewels, but there are two things you must do. If you don't, I'll wreck your Crystal Palace and fill up the whole Qiantang River!"

"What two things? Tell me."

"First, you must send my mother back right away. Second, you must not raise the tide arbitrarily just because the fancy strikes you. Hereafter, the tide must follow the course of the river and it must only rise to the foot of the hill here."

The Dragon King had absolutely no desire to obey these conditions but, as he was afraid that Six Harmonies might really fill in the river and smash his Crystal Palace, he finally had no choice but to agree.

The Dragon King sent Six Harmonies' mother back right away, and how joyous it made him feel! Mother and son went home happily together.

From then on, the tide in the Qiantang River became more tame and it always stopped at the foot of the hill. Only on the eighteenth day of the eighth month the tide was stronger than usual. This is because the Dragon King, after having suffered a lesson from Six Harmonies, was afraid that his followers might make some mistake, so he personally came out to inspect the river once a year. When people perceived the temperance of the tide, they no longer feared the river. They reclaimed the land by the river and worked it into good fields that grew green crops.

In order to commemorate the fact that Six Harmonies subdued the Dragon King, they built a pagoda on the hill from which Six Harmonies moved the rocks. This then is the "Six Harmonies Pagoda."

Prince Qian Shoots the Tide

Beating the Dragon King

In the beginning, when the tide came in on the Qiantang River, just like the tides of other rivers, there were no breakers and no noise.

One year, a giant came to the Qiantang River. He was so tall he could step from one side of the river to the other side easily. He lived on Mount Shu in Xiaoshan County and he made salt by the firing process. Nobody knew what his real name was, but because he lived along the Qiantang River, he was called Great King Qian. Great King Qian was very strong. He often used his iron carrying pole to move many large stones to the river's edge, and soon they were piled into mountains.

One day, he went to get the salt that he had been firing on Mount Shu for the past three years and three months. However, the salt was just enough for one end of his carrying pole, so he had to tie a large piece of rock on the other end. When he tried lifting the carrying pole to his shoulder, he found it was well balanced, so he picked up the load and stepped over to the north shore. It was very hot then and because Great King Qian had just eaten lunch, he

was a bit tired. He put down his load to rest, but he had
fallen asleep before he knew it.

By coincidence, the Dragon King of the Eastern Sea was
just coming out on an inspection at this very moment, and
so the tide began to rise. The tide rose up and up and up,
until it reached the river bank and gradually melted the salt
that belonged to Great King Qian. The Dragon King sniffed
and smelt. Why was the water so salty? And still it became
saltier and saltier. The Dragon King finally could stand it no
longer, so he turned around and fled back into the sea.
However, when he fled back to sea, the water there turned
salty too.

As for Great King Qian, when he opened his eyes, waking
up from his nap, he noticed that the rock on one end of his
carrying pole was still there at Xiashi (today, the famous
Mount Xiashi). However, the salt at the other end of the
load was gone! He looked all over but was unable to find his
salt. When he lowered his head, he could tell by the smell
that the river water was all salty.

"Ah, no wonder!" he thought: "It was stolen by the
Dragon King of the Eastern Sea!"

Thereupon he lifted his carrying pole and started hitting
the sea water. At the first blow, all the fish, large and small,
died from the shock. At the second blow, the bottom of the
sea flipped up. At the third blow, the Dragon King emerged
from the water to beg for his life.

The troubled Dragon King of the Eastern Sea asked Great
King Qian why he was in such a rage.

"Where have you hidden the salt you stole from me?"

Only then did the Dragon King realize why the sea water
had become salty. He quickly begged forgiveness and told
Great King Qian how he must have accidentally melted the
salt when he came out to inspect the river, and how this
must have made the sea water turn salty.

This really made Great King Qian angry. He felt like beating the Dragon King to a pulp with his carrying pole. The Dragon King was so frightened he just kept kowtowing and begging forgiveness, and even promised to evaporate the sea water to get the salt to repay Great King Qian. He also promised to make a noise from then on whenever the tide was about to rise, so that Great King Qian would be able to hear it even if he should fall asleep. Great King Qian thought that these were two good conditions, so he forgave the Dragon King.

"From now on, the tide should begin to make a noise starting from here!" said King Qian, hurling his carrying pole all the way to Hangzhou Bay.

The Dragon King quickly agreed and Great King Qian walked away quite happy.

From that time on, as soon as the tide enters Hangzhou Bay it stretches its neck out to call: "Swish! Swish!" When the tide reaches the spot where Great King Qian once sat, it stretches its neck out the farthest and shouts the loudest. This spot is present day Haining, and this is how the well-known "Qiantang River Tide" came to be.

Prince Qian Shoots the Tide

The tide waters of the Qiantang River always used to be very strong. The tide was high and it would rush and batter hard. As a result, the dikes along the banks were difficult to maintain. By the time one side was fixed, the other side would be destroyed. One can get an idea of the damage it brought to people in those days from the popular saying: "It takes a bushel of gold to repair the Yellow River, and a bushel of silver to repair the Qiantang every day."

Towards the end of the Tang Dynasty, there was a Prince of Wuyue named Qian Liu who was incomparably brave and strong. People at the time all called him Prince Qian.

When Prince Qian governed Hangzhou, he felt that all other matters were easy to handle compared to the task of keeping the dikes of the Qiantang River in good order, which was truly a headache. Every time the dike was repaired, it was destroyed by the resurging tide waters. Since the tide came once in the morning and once in the evening, there was absolutely no way of keeping the dikes in good repair.

The people under Prince Qian were all worried and afraid

that he might become angry with them. They had to report to him: "Great Prince, let's not even try to repair the dikes any more. It is useless. There is a God of Tides in the river who is working against us, and each time we are almost finished repairing the dikes, he raises the wind and makes the tide break down our dikes."

When Prince Qian heard this, he was so angry that every one of his whiskers stiffened up and his eyes bulged open as wide as bronze bells. He shouted sternly: "Ah you! You worthless bunch of swine! Why didn't you haul this God of Tides up and kill him?"

"You can't do that! He is a deity and lives with the Dragon King in the sea! We have no way of finding him, because he rides inside the tide and rolls within the waves. We are just ordinary people. We can neither see him nor catch him. Even if you went to look for him in an iron boat, those waves would soon swallow it up." The others answered in consternation.

Listening to this, Prince Qian became so angry that sparks flew from his eyes. "Bah! Do you mean to say we should let this God of Tides stir up all the trouble he wants? Never!" he shouted.

After thinking it over a while, Prince Qian said: "Fine, I'll go and take care of him myself. Have ten thousand archers assembled beside the river on the eighteenth of the eighth month. I really must meet this God of Tides!"

Why do you suppose he chose the eighteenth of the eighth month for this occasion? It was because this day was the birthday of the God of Tides. On this day, the waves were especially high and the tide waters were strong and vicious enough to overturn the whole landscape. Furthermore, on that day the God of Tides would gallop about on the waves, riding on a white horse.

On the eighteenth of the eighth month, a royal platform

was set up along the bank of the Qiantang River. Prince Qian arrived early to observe from the platform the movements of the tide and to wait for the God of Tides to appear. However, the best ten thousand archers only came trickling in one by one, and it was taking a long time for them to get assembled. When Prince Qian noticed this, he ordered that they be gathered by the river and form ranks immediately.

At this point, a general came forward and knelt down: "Great Prince! These men have to pass by Gemstone Mountain to get here. The mountain path is very narrow and only one person can pass through at a time, after which they have to climb up and down the hill; that's why they are arriving so slowly."

"Oh, bah! This is going to delay the annihilation of the God of Tides!"

He immediately jumped on his swift horse and flew off to Gemstone Mountain, where he found the situation just as it was described to him. He ran straight up the hill to survey the surroundings. He noticed there was a crack on the south side of the mountain. He sat down, put his feet into the crack, and pushed hard. Aha! He split the mountain open so that a wide path appeared in the middle. When the archers saw this, they all cheered and shouted. After this, it took no time at all for the archers to gather by the river using this path. From that time on, this place has been called "Push-open Peak." Prince Qian's huge foot prints are still deeply impressed on the stone walls.

Prince Qian then made the rounds once on his horse, and when he returned to the platform, all ten thousand archers were set up. Each and every one of them was brave and full of spirit, holding bow and arrow in hand and watching the river waters. All the people who lived by the river had suffered the damage of the tides and all had willingly contributed to the repairing of the dikes and the effort to control the floods. Hearing now that Prince Qian was going to shoot the God of Tides, they all rushed over to watch and to give him moral support. The doors of every household were shut as everyone came out. People crowded tightly along the length of the miles and miles of river bank. Seeing this, Prince Qian was even more encouraged and quickly asked to have ink and a writing brush brought over.

He wrote two lines:

Reporting to the God of Tides and his administration:

Let the Qiantang River be used for the good of its town.

He threw these lines into the river and shouted: "Hey! God of Tides, listen to me! If you agree, then you must not let the tides swell. If your tides continue to swell, then you mustn't blame me for being ruthless!"

When the people and the archers heard this, they raised a cheer that roared like thunder. Then everyone nervously watched the movements of the river water.

The God of Tides paid no attention to the warning given by Prince Qian. In a moment, everyone could see a white line rolling over from afar. It came faster and faster, and more and more fiercely. As it came nearer, like an exploding iceberg, like a collapsing mountain of snow, it charged furiously toward the royal platform. When Prince Qian saw this, he roared the command: "Shoot!" As soon as the word left his lips, he let the first arrow fly.

At this point, all ten thousand archers let fly ten thousand arrows, aiming at the waves. The people all stamped their feet and cheered their encouragement. Ten thousand arrows were followed by another ten thousand; ten thousand more were again followed by another ten thousand. "Shoot, shoot, shoot!" Thirty thousand arrows flew in the blink of an eye and the waves were so frightened they did not dare to charge at the banks.

"Follow them! Shoot!" Prince Qian gave another command and the waves twisted and turned and fled to the southwest until, finally, all disappeared without a trace. Therefore, to this very day, the tide always peters out to almost nothing at Six Harmonies Pagoda. The waters always twist and turn and flow away in front of the pagoda, just like the character " 之 *(zhi)."* Hence, people also call this place the "Zhi River."

It was only from that time that dikes could be built along the river. In order to commemorate the great achievement of Prince Qian, people named the dikes by the river *Qiantang* (The Qian Embankment).

The Ancestors of Tea

Long ago, Dragon Well was nothing but a small, lonely, neglected village. Ten or so households were sparsely scattered in the valley. They planted bamboo on the more distant hills and grains on those nearby. Their life was harsh all year round.

On the edge of the village, there was a run-down hut which resisted neither wind nor rain, in which there lived an old granny. She was quite old, so she could not climb the hills or toil in the fields. All she could do was take care of the eighteen old tea plants that grew at the back of her hut. These were planted when her "old man" was still alive, so they were several dozen years old by now. These tea plants had not received the best of care, and they lacked fertilizer, so there were very few new leaves. Each year the granny could pick no more than a few pounds of old tea leaves.

The old granny was a kind soul. She chose to skimp and endure discomfort in her own daily life so as to save some tea leaves every year; with these she would boil a pot of tea every day, and set up two benches under her awning so that the travelers who had to climb up and down the hills and peaks could rest and quench their thirst.

One year, on New Year's Eve, a heavy snow was falling. All her neighbors to the left and right had more or less prepared some new year's things for the festive occasion. But the old granny was really very poor; her rice container was almost empty and all that was left in the whole hut was some old tea leaves. However, she still observed her usual custom and early in the morning put a handful of tea leaves in the pot and built a fire to make a pot of tea. Then she heard the door open with a "creak," and there was an old man covered with snow.

The old granny quickly stood up to welcome him: "Old Grandpa, the wind is strong and the snow is heavy. Come on inside and rest a bit."

The old man dusted off the snow and came into the room. While facing the fire in the stove, he started a conversation with her: "What are you cooking in the pot, Granny?"

"I'm boiling some tea!"

"It's New Year's Eve. Tomorrow is New Year's Day. Everybody else is busy cooking sacrificial meats for the celebration. Why are you making tea?"

"Well," she sighed, "this lonely old woman is very poor. I can't afford to buy blessings with sacrificial meats, so I just make tea for the travelers every day."

"Poor! You're not poor! There's a treasure right in front of your house," laughed the old man after listening to the old lady.

The old granny was surprised. She poked her head out to look around and found that everything was the same as always outside. There were two old benches under the awning of pine needles and an old broken stone mortar filled with several years of garbage. Everything was the same as ever.

The old man walked over and pointed at the broken mortar: "There, there is the treasure!"

The old granny thought the old man was joking with her, so she smiled; "An old stone mortar! How could that be a treasure! If you like it, you may have it."

"Oh, but how could I take your treasure without paying you for it! Sell it to me. I'll go now and find someone to come and get it." So saying, the old man left, braving the heavy snow.

Old granny took a look at the broken stone mortar: "This mortar is filthy. How are they going to move it?" So thinking, she carried all the garbage in the mortar away with a dust pan and buried it under the eighteen old tea plants near their roots. Then she went to Dragon Well, brought back a bucket of clear water, washed the stone mortar nice and clean, then poured the dirty water next to the tea plants.

Just as she was finished cleaning the mortar, the old man came back with some other people. When he arrived at the door, he started shouting: "Good heavens! What happened to the treasure? Where is the treasure?"

The old granny was confused. She pointed to the broken stone mortar and said: "Umm .... Isn't it right here?"

"No, what did you do with the stuff that was in it?"

"I threw it over by the tea plants."

The old man walked to the back of the hut and saw that what she said was true. He could not help stamping his feet: "Pity! What a pity! The precious part of that broken mortar is in the old garbage. Since you've already buried it, we'll just have to let it benefit those eighteen plants." Then he left with the people he had brought with him.

New Year came after New Year's Eve, and soon spring was here. This year, unlike before, the eighteen old tea plants behind the granny's hut were densely laden with tender green shoots. The tea leaves gathered from them were fine, tender and fragrant.

When the neighbors saw that the old granny's tea plants were so good, they all cleared away the bamboo, harvested their grain, and started planting tea on every hill, far and near, with the seeds from those eighteen old tea plants. Year after year, they grew more and more abundant and flourishing. Later on, all the hills and fields around Dragon Well came to be full of tea plants.

Since the tea leaves produced in this area are so fine, tender and fragrant, and have a uniquely delicious flavor, "Dragon Well Tea" has become known far and wide.

Even today, the tea farmers all claim that the eighteen tea plants behind the old granny's hut were the ancestors of Dragon Well Tea.

The Black Dragon

A long time ago, there lived a certain family at Arbutus Peak. Both the husband and the wife were over sixty years old but they only had one son, and he was only twelve. Their son was handsome and healthy. He had been a good boy ever since he was little and was able to help his parents from the time he was seven or eight years old. His father was happy with him and so was his mother, so they named him Happy. All the local villagers praised him for being a good boy.

The old couple doted on their son and did not want him to become "a wide-eyed blind man"— i.e., an illiterate —so they sent him to the little school in the village temple to study.

One day, when lessons were over, a dozen or so boys rushed out of the village to play, like a swarm of bees. After Happy played with his friends for a while, he noticed that smoke was starting to rise from the village chimneys. Thinking it was time that his mother would be making lunch, he hurried on home.

As soon as he stepped into the house, he heard his

mother call: "Happy! The water jar is empty. Go and fetch
some water, will you?"

Happy said yes and went out with a bucket after putting
his school bag down.When he came to the stream,he saw two
mudfish swimming back and forth, fighting for a pearl.
Thinking it was rather curious, he chased away the mudfish
and picked up the pearl.

After drawing the water, Happy started back to home
cheerily with the bucket in one hand and the pearl in the
other. When the other children learned that he had picked
up something interesting, they all came skipping and
hopping over, wanting to see it. Happy was afraid that if
they took it, they might not return it to him, so he held the
pearl tightly in his fist and raised it up high. But the
children would not give in, and with a great yell they all
rushed upon him together to snatch the pearl. Happy could
not possibly defend himself against so many children, so he
quickly popped the pearl into his mouth. The children then
started to pinch his face and tried to force open his mouth;
they even tickled him under his arms. Happy wanted to yell
to his mother for help, but when he opened his mouth, he
gulped down the pearl before he could utter a sound.

After swallowing the pearl, Happy thought it was really a
pity to have lost it. When he came home, his mother had
not yet finished cooking lunch. He had nothing to do before
lunch, so he opened up his school bag and took out the
inkstone and the writing brush; he put some water in the
inkstone and ground some ink, then sat properly in front of
his desk to practise writing.

After a while, when his mother brought him his lunch,
she was shocked to discover that her son's face was so
swollen that it had turned purple. His eyes were bulging out
like two bronze bells. He had sprouted two crooked horns
on his head, and his mouth opened all the way back to his

ears. There was a roaring noise in his throat like thunder and his body had grown very long. As it happened, the thing that Happy had swallowed was a dragon pearl — he had turned into a dragon.

A dragon needs water in order to fly! Happy bowed his head down to the inkstone and licked up the ink. Immediately he transformed into a totally ink-black dragon. The black dragon then crashed out of the house and flew away; higher and higher it flew, until the dragon tail brushed against Arbutus Peak. Suddenly, dark clouds covered the sun, wild winds screamed, thunder roared, and heavy rains poured down. The black dragon flew towards the east, braving the clouds and fog.

Now this son had been the treasure of his parents. How could they bear to let him fly away! The old couple stumbled out of their house into the wild winds and rain. As they chased, they cried:

"Happy, come back!"

"Happy, come back!"

Father called and then mother shouted. One cry followed another. Every time the black dragon heard a call, he would stop. His father and his mother each called nine times, and altogether the black dragon stopped and turned his head around to look back eighteen times. At this point, he had already flown to the Qiantang River. He lowered himself into the river and followed it out to the Eastern Sea.

Now the tail of this black dragon was composed of nine sections; when he dragged his tail over Arbutus Peak, he carved nine ditches that later were filled with rainwater and trickled into nine streams. The black dragon stopped and turned his head around eighteen times; at those places where he stopped and turned his head around, eighteen beaches were formed. These, then, are the famous "Nine Streams and Eighteen Beaches."

Lady Silkworm

It is said that Lady Silkworm lived in the valley halfway up the mountain.

Years and years ago, there lived at Buddha Bridge in Hangzhou a smart and capable little girl called Cutie. When Cutie was nine years old, her mother died, leaving her and her brother behind; their father remarried and the step-mother had the heart of a scorpion. She was vicious towards Cutie and her brother!

In this particular year, one day in deepest winter, the step-mother asked Cutie to go out in the bitter north wind with a bamboo basket on her back to cut some grass for the sheep. Now, where could there be any green grass on a day like this in the bitter cold of winter? Cutie searched from dawn till dusk and she looked from riverside to halfway up the mountain, but she could find no tender grass. She was cold and frightened, so she sat there halfway up the mountain and started to cry. As she was weeping, she suddenly heard a voice above her, saying:

"Want green grass? Go to the valley!
Want green grass? Go to the valley!"

Lady Silkworm

Cutie raised her head to see a bird with white head and neck, flapping its wings and flying off towards the valley. She stood up, wiped away her tears and followed the bird. After turning a corner, the bird disappeared, and all she could see was a straight old pine tree standing at the entrance to the valley. The green tree was like an umbrella covering the entrance.

Cutie pushed the branches out of her way; on the other side of the tree, everything brightened before her eyes. She saw a winding brook gurgling along its way; flowers were red and grass was green along the brook, so beautiful that it was just like spring.

When she saw the green grass, it was as though she had discovered a treasure, and she bent down to cut it. She was cutting and walking until, without knowing it, she had come to the end of the brook, her bamboo basket now full of green grass. She stood up to wipe the sweat off her brow, when she saw not far in front of her a lady wearing a white blouse and white skirt. The lady was carrying a fine bamboo basket and was beckoning to her.

The lady in white smiled at Cutie: "Little girl, what a rare visitor you are! Won't you come and stay with us for a few days?"

Cutie raised her eyes and found a totally different world. There were rows of neat houses with white-washed walls and white-tiled roofs. There was a low forest in front of the houses. The leaves on the trees were so green, and larger than the palm of your hand. There were also many other ladies in white who were carrying fine bamboo baskets. They were smiling, singing and picking the tender green leaves from the trees.

Cutie was pleased and decided to stay.

Thereafter, Cutie worked together with the ladies in white. During the day, they picked tender green leaves in the low forest, and fed them to a kind of small snowy white worms at night. Slowly, the little worms would grow up and spew out silk to form snow white little "walnuts." The lady in white then taught Cutie how to reel the shining bright silk from these white "walnuts," and taught her how to dye the silk using seeds from various trees: dark blue seeds would turn the silk blue; red seeds would turn the silk vermilion; yellow seeds would turn it golden, and so on. The lady in white also told Cutie that these snow white worms were called "heavenly worms," and the leaves they ate were called mulberry leaves. All this colorful silk would be used to embroider a dragon coat for the Heavenly Emperor, and by the Weaving Maid to weave colorful clouds.

Cutie stayed in the valley with the ladies in white, picking mulberry leaves, feeding "heavenly worms," and reeling silk. Days passed by very quickly and three months were gone before she knew it.

On this particular day, Cutie suddenly thought of her brother: "Why not ask my brother to come here and enjoy some happy times too?"

Next day, before she even had time to tell the lady in white, she rushed homeward. Just before she left, Cutie found a piece of white paper covered with eggs of the "heavenly worms," and also took two bags of mulberry seeds. As she walked, she dropped the seeds along the road. She thought to herself: "Tomorrow I'll come back following the trail of the mulberry seeds."

When Cutie reached home, she found that her father had grown old and her brother into a young man.

"Cutie! Why did you not come home for fifteen years? Where have you been all these years?" Her father asked, happy and sad at the same time.

Cutie then told her father the whole story of how she went up the mountain and how she met the lady in white.

When their neighbors learned this they all came to see her, and told her that it must have been the fairy maiden that she had met.

Next morning, Cutie wanted to go back to the valley to take another look. Just as she stepped outside the door, she saw that the road was lined with low green trees. As a matter of fact all the mulberry seeds she dropped had grown into trees. She walked along the trail of low trees until she came to the valley. The old pine tree still stood there like an umbrella covering the entrance, but she could no longer find a way to get around it.

Just as Cutie was staring at the old pine tree, that same bird with the white head and white neck suddenly flew out from behind the tree. It screamed:

"Cutie stole the treasure!
Cutie stole the treasure!"

Then Cutie remembered that she had left without even telling the lady in white and that she had taken the eggs and two bags of mulberry seeds. The lady in white must have become angry with her and hidden the path so that she could not return. She could only go back home. When the eggs of the "heavenly worms" were hatched, she picked tender mulberry leaves to feed them, and thus started to raise the worms.

It was from that time that we first had the "heavenly worms." Later, since these worms all produce silk, people started to call them "silkworms." It was said that the lady in white whom Cutie met in the valley was none other than Lady Silkworm, who presides over cocoons and the harvesting of silk.

The Hua Pond

Long, long ago, the vast expanse of wasteland outside Jubilant Spring Gate was government property. One year, Grand Tutor Hua of the Imperial Court sent his steward, Smelly Nose, to Hangzhou. Smelly Nose, riding on horseback, galloped a circle around the wasteland, and this was made the property of the Hua family. Grand Tutor Hua further had notices posted by the four city gates of Hangzhou, recruiting tenant farmers to reclaim the wasteland. The notices said that if the farmers could make the land productive, no rent would be charged within ten years.

The poor people all straightened their fingers to count: The first year, nothing; the second year, half a harvest; the third year, seventy percent of a full harvest .... Ah, was there ever such a kind-hearted landlord in the world?

Now it happened that a man and wife moved in from another province. They were in a hurry to find a place to settle down, so without asking any further questions, they affixed their finger prints to the contract of Grand Tutor Hua. They came out beyond Jubilant Spring Gate and found a deep pond, by which they put up a thatched hut and started to work day and night with all their strength to reclaim the wasteland.

In December, deep in the winter of that year, the wife was going to have a baby. Not a single relative brought any brown sugar to this isolated little hut; not a single neighbor brought a little ginger broth for the expectant mother. There was only the husband watching over his wife, and he was walking in circles, so great was his anxiety. Swoosh! The north wind blew open the door of the hut, so the husband went over to fasten it. Swoosh! Again the north wind blew open the door, and again the husband went to fasten it. Swoosh! For the third time, the door was blown open. Just as the husband had bolted the door for the third time, a boy was born with a loud "Wah!"

"I had to bolt the door three times before he was born, let's just call him Three Bolts!" he said to his wife.

The husband thought his son was growing too slowly, so he said: "Three Bolts! Hurry and grow up, your father's back is almost bent with age!"

Three Bolts grew taller at once.

The wife also thought he was growing up too slowly, so she said: "Three Bolts! Hurry and grow up. My eyes are getting blurred with age!"

Three Bolts again grew taller in a flash. By now this new born child was already bigger than a seven or eight year old boy, and more mature than a ten year old. He could help with work both inside and outside the house.

When Three Bolts helped his father till the land, a patch of dark cloud always followed him, so even the hottest sun in June could not harm him. When he went to fetch water for his mother, he had only to blow into the buckets, and the two buckets would be filled with water. People all said that he was no ordinary child. Three Bolts was a dragon in human form.

Since Three Bolts' father had put his finger prints on Grand Tutor Hua's contract, other poor people had also become tenants, and moved to live on the wasteland. Gradually, twenty or thirty households had settled down along the pond and a small village was formed. People hoed and people raked, and soon the wasteland was converted. In the east there were beautiful green fields and in the west there was lush green land. Willow branches waved in the wind and a hundred kinds of flowers smiled in the breeze. It was a beautiful scene.

In the third spring, when the fields were tilled and the shoots put in, Three Bolts' father died, having spent his last bit of strength. His mother was so sad that she cried until both her eyes were blind. From them on, Three Bolts earned the living for his mother and himself by herding one family's cow or cutting fodder for another family.

Soon, Grand Tutor Hua retired and returned to his native Hangzhou. When he saw that this wasteland had been transformed into such a beautiful place, he wanted it back to build a mansion for his remaining years.

Smelly Nose rushed into the village with his people and forced the tenant farmers to move away immediately.

The tenants all shouted: "Wasn't it made clear that no rent was to be demanded within ten years?"

Smelly Nose laughed slyly: "It was within ten years all right! One year is within ten years; half a year is within ten years; but it has now been three years! Our boss has been kind enough already!"

He gave the order, and his people started tearing down the houses. When they came to Three Bolts' house, he would not let them. As if gone mad, he dashed at Smelly Nose and started to scratch and bite him. Smelly Nose was terrified. He ordered that Three Bolts be tied up, then had him fastened to a rock and dropped into the deep pond.

Smelly Nose then started a fire in which Three Bolts' blind mother died in the hut.

When Smelly Nose and his people left, the neighbors all rushed to the pond to look for Three Bolts' body. They tried a long time, but they could not find his corpse. Someone dived into the water to look around and found a bottomless hole in the middle of the pond.

Very soon after this, a splendid mansion was built on this piece of land. The grounds inside the mansion were laid with tiles of gold, and the surrounding walls were made of silver bricks. The walls inside the rooms were inlaid with pearls and the beams were inlaid with white jade. It was really a splendid residence: "See the immortal's palace in heaven; behold the minister's home on earth!"

The building of the mansion was completed just in time for the Grand Tutor's sixtieth birthday. On this day, there were bright lamps and gay decorations all over the mansion and the atmosphere was extremely exciting. Grand Tutor Hua sat in his comfortable armchair as the officials and gentlemen who came to wish him a happy birthday all knelt on the floor, covering up the entire space. Just as this ceremony was over and they were about to be seated for the feast, Smelly Nose came stumbling and crawling in.

"Grand Tutor, Your Honor! Something's wrong! Two cypress trees have suddenly sprouted up in the backyard. Must be some monster!" He shouted frantically.

Grand Tutor Hua did not believe him, so he went to the backyard together with the officials and gentlemen to have a look. Indeed: Standing right there were two bare cypress tree trunks.

One official quickly tried to save the situation by saying something nice: "This is a blessing sent down from heaven. May the Grand Tutor's life be as long as the evergreen pines and cypresses — forever green ...."

Before he could finish his speech, the tree trunks started to shoot upward. "Boom!" A giant dragon flew out of the ground. These tree trunks were the dragon's giant horns, and the gigantic dragon was none other than Three Bolts, who had come back to avenge himself!

The giant dragon turned around, head swinging and tail sweeping, and caused the entire mansion of the Grand Tutor to sink underground. The site of the mansion then turned into a huge pond, dozens of acres in circumference, in which Grand Tutor Hua and the officials and gentlemen were all drowned.

The poor tenants whom Hua had driven away came back from all directions and settled down around the pond. They tilled the land and planted trees and flowers, with the result that the place became more and more beautiful year by year.

People named this place "The Hua Pond" because the Hua mansion had sunk beneath it. Others, seeing that the scenery here was so excellent, called it "Little West Lake."

Yuchi Gong and the Monk

In the lower section of the city of Hangzhou there is an Immortal Forest Monastery, which boasts only a main hall but lacks a proper mountain entrance. This awkward temple and monastery is said to have been built during the time of Emperor Taizong (reigned 627-649) of the Tang Dynasty.

In his childhood, Taizong was a very sickly boy. His father, afraid that he might die prematurely, made him take on a Buddhist monk by the name of Immortal Forest as his master. Years later, Taizong subdued his enemies and became Emperor. The monk Immortal Forest had heard that Hangzhou was a beautiful place, so he asked the Emperor to have a huge monastery built for him in Hangzhou, into which he would retire. As the monk was his spiritual master, Taizong could not very well refuse such a request, so he sent the great general Yuchi Gong (585-658) to Hangzhou to supervise the building of this huge monastery.

Immortal Forest came to Hangzhou with Yuchi Gong, and they started to discuss the size of this monastery.

Immortal Forest said: "This monastery will be for the retirement of the Emperor's spiritual master, and is thus very special. The land should be at least a couple of miles long!"

Yuchi Gong was flabbergasted: "Who has ever seen a monastery of that size! Before I became a general, when I was only the apprentice of a blacksmith, working with seven or eight other apprentices, our workshop was no more than fifty by fifty feet! You are nothing but an old monk. You'll be doing nothing besides eating, sleeping, and chanting sutras. What do you want a big place like that for? I'll give you a piece of land five hundred by five hundred feet; you simply cannot have more!"

Immortal Forest haggled to high heaven, and Yuchi Gong brought him right back down to earth. They argued from dawn to dusk without agreement.

Next morning Immortal Forest sent someone to invite Yuchi Gong to come and discuss matters. As soon as Yuchi Gong arrived and dismounted, he heard the monk yell from inside: "By Imperial Decree!" Hearing this, Yuchi Gong was obliged to kneel down and bow his head to receive the decree. The monk stood solemnly inside and started reading out the Imperial Decree, word by word, slowly, in a long drawn-out voice, so that a few dozen words took him about half an hour to read. He read it over and over, again and again, continuing from early morning until the noon hour.

Now Yuchi Gong was a dark and stoutly-built chap. He could take three days and three nights on a fast horse on the battlefield with no difficulty. On the other hand, having to kneel down for half a day without moving a muscle was just too much for him. He was sweating and aching all over, and was almost unable to stand up again.

When Immortal Forest finally finished reading the Imperial Decree, he said with a smile: "My general, have you heard everything clearly this time? The Imperial Decree states clearly that the greatest of monasteries should be built for my retirement. How could the greatest of monasteries be anything less than two miles by two miles in dimension?"

Yuchi Gong shook his head: "The Imperial Decree states that the monastery should be the greatest but it does not say that it need be two miles by two miles in dimension. I'm the Imperial Supervisor for the building of the monastery and I do not go back on my word. It is still to be five hundred by five hundred feet!"

They argued for another day with no result.

After another night, the monk sent someone to fetch Yuchi Gong again.

Yuchi Gong thought to himself: "This crafty monk made me kneel down for half a day. This time I'll give him a taste of his own medicine!" Whereupon he took the *ruyi* jade scepter out of his trunk and hid it under his gown, then set out on his horse.

As soon as Yuchi Gong dismounted, the old monk started to replay the same trick: "By Imperial Decree!" This time Yuchi Gong slowly walked into the room, seated himself in the armchair at the exact center of the room and, taking out his jade scepter, said: "Behold the scepter kindly bestowed on me by our Most Supreme Emperor (the Emperor's father). Kneel down and read your Imperial Decree!" As a matter of fact, this *ruyi* scepter had been bestowed on Yuchi Gong by the Emperor's father because of his great achievements in the building of the dynasty so as to insure that he would be treated with the greatest respect at all times.

The monk did not expect this to happen, so he knelt down and this time finished reading the Imperial Decree in a hurry. Then as he straightened his back, getting ready to stand up, Yuchi Gong said: "Wait, wait! My hearing is not so good! I still haven't heard it all clearly!" The monk had no choice but to kneel down and read it again. Yuchi Gong claimed he still did not hear it clearly, and asked the monk to read it over and over and over again. The monk was reading from early morning until nearly dusk and was almost out of breath. Thinking that this should suffice, Yuchi Gong told him to stand up.

After this, Immortal Forest knew that he was powerless, so he agreed on a lot five hundred by five hundred feet for the Immortal Forest Monastery.

After the monastery was built, Yuchi Gong got on his ebony piebald horse and started on his way back to the capital city. Immortal Forest was still indignant so, riding on a bald donkey, he came clip-clopping from behind in pursuit of Yuchi Gong, but not until the boundary of Haining County did he catch up with him.

"Great general, slow down a bit! I have something to discuss with you!" The monk yelled from behind.

Yuchi Gong slowed down his ebony piebald horse and asked him what he wanted.

"General, you forgot to have a mountain entrance built! Tell me now, who has ever heard of a monastery or temple without a mountain entrance?"

Yuchi Gong thought what he said was quite right, so he promised another hundred feet of land for the building of a mountain entrance. You would think this would be a good ending for the whole thing. The monk, however, created a further disturbance by asking that the mountain entrance be built two miles away from the main hall of the monastery.

"Why is this?"

"Don't you even understand this much?" The monk retorted: "This Immortal Forest Monastery is the very first monastery built since the beginning of the great Tang

Dynasty! If we build the mountain entrance farther away, the dynasty will last all the longer!" The monk was very serious about this.

Yuchi Gong was so enraged he spit hard on the monk: "Bah! Do you think the world of the Tang Dynasty, built by our blood and sweat, is only two miles long?"

Hearing this, the monk naturally thought that Yuchi Gong was going to allot him even more than two miles. He was so thrilled he almost fell off his bald donkey.

Yuchi Gong jumped off his horse and, using his weapon, the famous bamboo-shaped iron staff, marked off a piece of land one hundred feet by one hundred feet square. "Now, have the mountain entrance built here!" He climbed back on his horse and returned to the capital city.

This put the monk in an awkward position: He did not know whether to laugh or to cry. He had planned to trick Yuchi Gong with the idea of the longevity of the dynasty in order to obtain all the land within the two miles for himself. He could never have suspected that Yuchi Gong would have the mountain entrance built this far away! A whole prefecture and a county stood between Hangzhou and Haining. How could a monk be in charge of a piece of land this big? Immortal Forest's fantastic design fell through again!

Today, the Immortal Forest Monastery is still in the same condition as before: The monastery itself is in Hangzhou but its mountain entrance stands alone in Haining.

The Beancurd Bridges

In the upper part of Hangzhou there is a "Comfort Bridge" and on the same river, there are three "Beancurd Bridges" alongside it. These four bridges were built during the years of the Southern Song Dynasty (1127-1279) and they are more than eight hundred years old now.

When Yue Fei defeated the Tungus armies, he had in his ranks a general by the name of Wang Zuo who made Lu Wenlong surrender by intentionally injuring himself, and thus utterly defeated Jin Wushu. From then on, Wang Zuo had only one arm and could no longer engage in battle. Yue Fei recommended that he be awarded the title of Prince Comfort, and the Emperor promised to have a mansion built in Hangzhou for his retirement.

The mansion of Prince Comfort was to be built by a river. When the construction started, sand, lime, stone slabs, and lumber piled up along the river. There was no bridge over the river and the only ferry boat was now occupied by workers transporting building material. The local people were left with no way of crossing the river and this angered them, so they made up a little song:

"Prince Comfort, Prince Comfort,
Everybody is busy for your comfort!"

Wang Zuo heard about this when he returned to Hangzhou. He thought to himself: "Why would I need a huge mansion for myself? Wouldn't it be better to use the material to build a bridge so that everyone could enjoy the convenience?" Thus he ordered the workers first to choose the strongest bricks and stone slabs to build a bridge across the river, then use the remaining material to build a simple house for the princely residence.

When people learned that a bridge was to be built before the prince's residence, they all came to help. Many people contributed much strength, and a wide and smooth bridge was built over the river within a month.

Now that there was a bridge, it became very convenient for the people to cross the river. They were very happy, and they made a new song:

"Prince Comfort's kindness showed
When he made a bridge to ease the road."

Everybody and his brother sang it, until the words were spread and Comfort Bridge became very famous. Then the news traveled to the ears of the Prime Minister Qin Hui, and he became very jealous.

"How can he become so famous from the building of a single bridge! Now I'm going to build three bridges, each wider and higher than the other. I'll put my wealth up against Wang Zuo's and we'll see who is the richer!"

Qin Hui had only to say a few words and his officials started to run around so fast that they nearly broke their legs. They increased taxes; they called for corvée labor and had the people work day and night to build the bridges. After three whole months, on the same river, there appeared three bridges alongside Comfort Bridge, and indeed each one was wider and higher than the other. Qin Hui was very pleased and personally bestowed names on these three bridges, calling them: "Wealth Contesting *(Doufu)* Bridge One," "Wealth Contesting Bridge Two," and "Wealth Contesting Bridge Three."

Now a bridge is just there for the traffic, and one bridge is quite sufficient over one spot on a river. Why should there be so many! The people all hated Qin Hui so much that they would not even walk on his bridges.

Since "wealth contesting *(doufu)*" sounds very much like "beancurd *(doufu),*" people called those three bridges the "Beancurd Bridges" to ridicule Qin Hui, and this name has lasted until now.

Plum Blossom Monument

Years and years ago, there lived in Hangzhou a very skilful and smart old stone cutter who spent his life chipping and carving stones, up to the time when his hair and his beard were all white. He had nothing else but this superb craftsmanship, and he became very well-known in Hangzhou, Jiaxing and Huzhou prefectures. This stone cutter was already an old man, his back was bent and his eyes were blurred but still he would go to the mountains to work every day as he always had.

One day, the old stone cutter found a shiny white stone at the foot of South Mountain. He seemed to perceive the vague shadow of a tree on the rock. He suspected his eyes were blurry, so he took another careful look. It's true! There was clearly the shadow of a plum tree, so real it seemed to have grown on the rock. He felt it with his hands; it was flat and smooth. It was just like a piece of white brocade with a design faintly traced on the surface before a girl had started to embroider it. The more he looked, the more he liked it; the more he liked it, the harder it became for him to leave it. Finally, he used all his strength to dig it out and carried it home on his back, step by stumbling step.

The old stone cutter gazed at it for three months, felt it for three months and contemplated it for another three months before he finally started to carve it. How hard the stone was! When he chipped at it, only a little powder would be loosened; when he hammered on it, just a few sparks would fly up. However, he would not give up and was never discouraged. He just kept on chipping and hammering, hammering and chipping, on and on. In ten days, he had carved a flower petal, and in one hundred days, he had carved a flower. One month and then another passed; a year and another year passed. The old stone cutter worked day and night without ever stopping until finally, he had carved the whole plum tree on the surface of the rock.

The plum tree was finished. What beautiful blossoms! They seemed to wave in the spring breeze, facing the rosy morning glow. Like white jade, they covered the whole tree. The old stone cutter, having now exhausted all within himself, died beside the tree.

He had no children and left behind no property. Everybody respected him and they gave him a burial in a public cemetery, placing the last plum blossom monument that he had carved on his grave.

Then, after many years, something strange happened: The plum blossoms on the monument began to bloom and wither. Every spring, when the plum blossoms on other trees were just beginning to bud, those on this tree were already in full bloom. In the summer, when the leaves on other plum trees were just beginning to show a little green, this tree was already covered with green leaves. By autumn, when no leaves at all were left on other plum trees, those on this tree were just beginning to fall. In winter, when the northwest wind made other plum trees bend in all directions, the one on the stone monument stood still and upright.

This stone monument could even forecast the weather: If it was going to be a fine day, the monument would appear shining bright. If it was going to be overcast, the monument would be foggy and damp. If it was going to rain, the stone would be gray and wet. People learned about the weather and the seasons from this stone, so that farmers could tell when to start their farming without delay, and travelers could be sure whether or not to set out on the road. Therefore, they all loved the stone and looked upon it as a treasure.

One spring, an important official came to Hangzhou. He had long ago heard about this marvelous stone monument so, not long after arriving at Hangzhou, he took some of his people and went to the old stone cutter's grave. He took a look and found that indeed the plum tree was in full bloom. After he went back, he sought advice from his villainous advisor, then had the yamen built around the old stone cutter's grave, and then built a fence that encircled the monument within his garden. He even shamelessly sent out a proclamation: "This is now official land that belongs to the government, so ordinary people are not allowed to enter."

It was really amazing! Within two days after the stone monument had been fenced in the official garden, it started to wither. Later on, no matter how the weather might change, the stone remained gray and wet. Gradually, moss took over the whole monument, making the stone not only dull, but truly ugly. Because of this, the official could neither eat nor sleep for all his anger and distress. He was reduced to walking circles in the garden.

At this time, his advisor came over with a proposal: "My master, this must have happened because the land here is too damp. If you have a fire built at the foot of the monument, when it gets drier, it will improve."

The official thought this was a good idea, so he had firewood and charcoal brought over and had a fire started on the stone cutter's grave. But just as soon as the flames licked the stone monument, it exploded with an ear-splitting "Boom!" Roaring flames were shot into the distance, and in a twinkling, the yamen and the whole garden were ablaze. The official and his advisor did not even have time to flee, and perished in the flames. The fire burned on for three days and three nights until the whole yamen was burnt down, and only half a charred flag pole remained in front. The stone monument was also lost in the fire.

To this very day, two place names, "Plum Blossom Monument" and "Burnt Flag Pole," still appear in the eastern part of Hangzhou.

The First Well Spring of Mount Wu

Many, many years ago, there simply were no wells in Hangzhou. At that time, there were good and regular rains, so not a family ever lacked water.

Unexpectedly one year, the weather changed: There was not a cloud to be seen in the vast expanse of sky and for several months not a drop of rain fell. It was so hot that the water in West Lake dried up and the fields all cracked. There was not even water for drinking. The government was afraid that people might stir up trouble, so many monks and priests were invited and altars were erected for them to perform their prayers. At this time, the people were also forced to come, kneel down and kowtow.

One old man who was made to come refused to kneel down for anything. This angered the officials and they arrested him. They held him in "contempt of the government" and were going to execute him.

The old man, however, was not frightened. On the contrary, he threw his head back and laughed: "I've lived for eighty years; death is nothing to me! But it would be a pity for the people of Hangzhou, for they'll be without water to drink, and you'll die of thirst with them! If you just give me three days, I can definitely find a source of water."

Hearing this, the officials thought to themselves: "This just might be true! We'll let him look for it. If he finds water, everything will be fine. If he doesn't, we can still kill him." So they agreed to give him three days.

When the old man went home, he called to his fifty-year-old son: "Hurry up and make me a bamboo sedan chair!"

"Where are you going in the sedan chair, Father?"

"I'm old and can't walk too far. I'm going to ride in the sedan chair to look for a water source!"

His son finished making the sedan chair.

The old man went to the vegetable garden and called to his twenty-year-old grandson: "Hurry up and get two bamboo poles to carry me in the sedan chair!"

"Where are you going, Grandpa?"

"When I stand up high, I shall be able to see far and wide. You and your father are going to carry me up to the city walls."

His grandson brought the bamboo poles, then son and grandson carried him up to the city walls of Hangzhou and walked back and forth upon them. They made three rounds in one day and nine rounds in three days on the walls. Finally he noticed that at the foot of Mount Wu (also known as City God Mountain), there were billows of something that looked neither like smoke nor fog, but kept on puffing and rising up. When it reached the sky, it formed a shiny white patch of cloud.

Pointing to the patch of cloud, the old man told his son and grandson: "Below that patch of cloud over there where the foggy smoke is rising, that is a dragon's pulse. There is a dragon breathing under the ground."

The old man assembled many people to dig a well at the

foot of City God Mountain. They dug and dug and dug down for thirty-three feet, but there was not a drop of water at the bottom! When the officials saw that the bottom of the well was dry, they had the old man beheaded without further ado.

His son and grandson cried bitterly for a long time, then buried the old man's body. The grandson, with tears in his eyes, supported his father as they both climbed atop the city walls to walk around again. They circled back and forth for another three days. They searched and searched for nine whole rounds. They noticed that the foggy smoke had grown even thicker where the well had been dug at the foot of City God Mountain. The shiny white patch of cloud in the sky also grew much larger.

Pointing to the patch of cloud, the father said to his son: "The place where the foggy smoke is coming out is a dragon's pulse after all. Your grandfather did find the right place!"

Again they gathered many people to dig farther down where they had begun to dig last time. Deeper and deeper they dug for another thirty-three feet. Yet there was still not a drop of water at the bottom! When the officials learned of this, they arrested the old man's son and beheaded him too, without so much as a question.

The grandson cried bitterly for a long time, then buried his father next to his grandfather's grave. Now he alone was left in the family. Lonely and sad, he ascended the city walls by himself and made the rounds as his grandfather and father had done before him. He walked back and forth for three days, and searched in all directions for nine rounds. He saw that the foggy smoke was even thicker than before and the patch of shiny white cloud in the sky was larger than ever before.

Pointing to the patch of cloud, the grandson said to

himself: "The place where the foggy smoke rises below the cloud is definitely the dragon pulse. Grandpa, Father, you were wronged!"

Again he gathered people to continue digging the same well. Digging deeper and deeper, they dug for another thirty-three feet, until they came to a bulging rock and could dig down no further.

The grandson felt back and forth at the bottom of the ninety-nine-foot deep well, but everywhere he touched, it was dry. Then he felt a big round bulging rock which seemed to be the dragon's eye.

He was desperate and shouted: "Dragon, oh dragon! Why don't you open your eyes? There is no rain from the sky and the earth does not give water. How are people supposed to live? I'm going to fight you to the finish today!" So saying, he dashed headlong at the bulging rock. "Bang! Crash!" With this thunderous noise, the rock cracked open and water came gurgling forth from the crack. Soon, the ninety-nine-foot deep well was filled to the brim.

The clear and pure water lifted the grandson to the top, but he had already died. People cried bitterly for a long time, then they buried him next to the graves of his grandfather and his father.

People have never had to worry for lack of drinking water since this well came about.

Later, they started to dig wells in other locations in the same manner, and gradually more and more wells appeared in Hangzhou. However, none of the later wells was as big and deep as the first one. Therefore, people called it "The First Well Spring of Mount Wu" and called the lane at the foot of the mountain "Big Well Lane."

Immortal Gazing Bridge

Years ago, there was a nameless stone bridge next to the drum tower in Hangzhou. Beside the bridge there was a doctor who specialized in treating sores and boils. He had a wide forehead, thick eye-brows, a high-bridged nose, wide mouth and a dark face that was covered with a beard. Both of his legs were covered with sores and boils and he was lame, one of his legs being shorter than the other. He set up a large umbrella beside the bridge and placed a broken medicine chest under the umbrella. He practised medicine under the umbrella during the day and lay on the chest to sleep at night.

At first, when people saw his looks, no one believed that he could actually cure an illness. Later on, someone with a gangrenous foot came to see him, thinking that he had nothing to lose since no one else had been able to heal him after three years of treatment. The doctor gave this man a dogskin plaster to put on his foot, and unexpectedly, the foot was healed in three days. This news traveled, and more and more people came for treatment under the umbrella. With this single kind of dogskin plaster, the doctor had healed many sores and boils, and his fame soon thundered through the city of Hangzhou. People gave him the nickname of "Hua Tuo's Peer," Hua Tuo being a famous physician of ancient times.

As Hua Tuo's Peer became well-known, the "highly skilled doctors" and owners of the herbal medicine shops began to lose business. They were so angry that they all came together and discussed the matter. They put together one thousand ounces of silver and gave it as a present to the Governor, demanding that Hua Tuo's Peer be driven out of Hangzhou.

After accepting the bribe, the Governor had Hua Tuo's Peer arrested.

When Hua Tuo's Peer was brought to court, he stood straight and firm.

The Governor rapped the gavel on his desk and shouted: "Bloody fool! Kneel before this Governor!"

"I am lame. My knee caps are too hard to permit kneeling down." Hua Tuo's Peer replied in a cool manner.

The Governor again rapped the gavel: "What is your name? Where did you come from?"

"I never had a name but people in Hangzhou gave me the nickname of Hua Tuo's Peer. As to where I came from, I just don't remember any more."

The Governor rolled his eyes around and then he burst out in laughter.

"Hua Tuo's Peer indeed! If your skill surpasses Hua Tuo, why didn't you first treat your own sores and boils?"

At this point, the Governor seemed to feel something climbing up his back. He felt so unbearably itchy that he quickly thrust his hand into his garment to feel what it was, but he could not feel anything.

Hua Tuo's Peer looked at him with cool eyes and smiled: "My Governor, Your Honor! How could you have been so smart all along and now suddenly not understand this? There are just so many professions in this world where people can only take care of others but never are able to take care of themselves! Why does a builder live in a hut? Why do people who raise silkworms wear tattered clothes? Why do farmers go hungry? Why does the government in charge of thieves accept bribes in secret? Why don't you ask about these and do something about them?"

The Governor was stumped and could not say a word, so he just kept on banging the gavel and shouting: "Slap his face! Put him in the death cell!"

After the court session, the Governor felt that the itch on his back had worsened, so he took off his garment and asked someone to take a look. It turned out that there was a small hard lump on his back. The more he scratched at the lump, the more itchy he became and the bigger it grew. Within an hour, it became a sore. He was in such pain that he rolled and yelled on his bed.

When his tutor learned about this, he came in and suggested, "Your Honor! I've heard that Hua Tuo's Peer is truly good at treating sores and boils! Let him treat you. After he has cured you, there will still be time for you to punish him."

The Governor could not bear the pain so he had Hua Tuo's Peer brought from prison. After Hua Tuo's Peer had examined the sore, he put a dogskin plaster on it.

By the next day, the sore on the Governor's back not only hadn't healed, but had become bigger, and blood and pus started to ooze from it. The stench was so foul that it penetrated three thick walls.

The Governor was in such a rage that he had Hua Tuo's Peer brought from prison before dawn.

"The boil on my back is getting worse! You must have put poison in your salve!"

"No hurry, simmer down. Let me take a look at the boil first." So saying, Hua Tuo's Peer opened up the patch and took a careful look. Then he wrinkled his brow and said: "This boil is small on the outside but very deep within. It rots from the inside out and is called 'Rot to the core.' There is no medicine capable of healing it. It is because you have been so utterly hard-hearted and without conscience that you contracted it. It has nothing to do with my medicine."

Now the Governor was both enraged and worried. "Chop his head off! Off with his head!" He shouted.

Soon, his breath became short and the whites of his eyes turned up and he died.

According to the Governor's last wish, the tutor convicted Hua Tuo's Peer of the crime of "Bewitching the multitudes with heresy" and sent him to the execution ground.

On his way to the execution ground, Hua Tuo's Peer walked over the stone bridge where he had set up his umbrella and medicine chest. People in the area knew that he had been wronged, so they all crowded around to exchange their views on the matter, with the result that the road was suddenly blocked.

Hua Tuo's Peer addressed the crowd: "Fellow townsmen! Since the officials insist on sending me back to Heaven, I have no choice but to go!" And so saying, he leaped up and threw himself off the bridge. The river water splashed and whirlpools started to turn at the spot. Suddenly, a puff of black smoke rose up, and there was Hua Tuo's Peer standing in the air, waving and nodding at the people below as he floated away with the black smoke.

Everybody said that Hua Tuo's Peer must have been an immortal. They could not forget him and so, at every festival, some of them would go to the stone bridge and gaze in the distance, hoping that he might come back to treat the sick again.

As time passed, this bridge came to be known as "Immortal Gazing Bridge."

Cat Bridge

L ong ago in Hangzhou, at the place where Lute Street turned a corner there was a bridge, alongside which there lived an old cobbler, who was utterly alone in the world except for his cat. This cat was nearly bald all over but for a few strands of hair. It was ugly as sin; it did not even know how to catch a mouse, and was so lazy that it wouldn't even mew. It just curled up at the cobbler's feet and slept quietly from morning till night.

The neighbors could not stand the sight of it and they told the cobbler: "Why don't you get rid of it? What's the use of such a lazy cat!"

The old cobbler would only shake his head: "My house is so quiet and lonely. It's nice to have a cat to keep me company."

One day as a treasure hunter passed by this place, the heel came off one of his boots, so he hopped into the old cobbler's shop to have it repaired. The treasure hunter sat there waiting for his boot, looking this way and that, when his eyes caught sight of the lazy cat at the cobbler's feet. He stared at the cat for a long time.

"Is this your cat?"

The old cobbler nodded his head.

"Sell it to me. I'll give you three hundred ounces of silver for it!"

The old cobbler thought he was joking, so he answered: "What would you want this cat for?"

"Never mind what I want this cat for. If you agree, you give me the cat and I'll give you the silver right now."

"I've never heard of anybody wanting to buy a cat for three hundred ounces of silver! No! I don't want to sell it!" The old cobbler shook his head.

Bystanders urged the old cobbler: "You've worked hard most of your life and never been able to save up three hundred ounces of silver. Here is your chance to get so much money you'll never be poor again for the rest of your life. Hurry up and sell this mangy cat!"

The old cobbler was still not convinced. He spoke slowly: "I've spent most of my life in poverty and I have survived. I just want to work and earn a bowl of rice to eat and that's enough for me. I do not expect to receive a windfall from this little cat!"

Everyone laughed at the old cobbler for being a fool.

Just as they were talking and arguing with each other, Mangy A Wu, the bully from Yangbatou, came passing by the place. When he heard about this good deal, he quickly pushed his way through the crowd and approached the treasure hunter: "Hello there, how are you! If it's this cat you want, there's no problem at all. If you just tell us what you want it for, I'll take care of buying it for you."

When people saw that Mangy A Wu the bully was here, they gradually dispersed. When the treasure hunter saw that this man seemed to have some influence here, he thought that he must be a man of means who surely could manage to get the cat.

"Sir, just take a good look at this cat. It has only a few yellow hairs on its body, but they shine in the sun, don't they? This is a Golden Silk Cat! You see, sir, there are twelve jade mice on top of Six Harmonies Pagoda by the Qiantang River. These jade mice come out to play on top of the pagoda at midnight; they are priceless treasures and only this Golden Silk Cat can catch them."

This whetted Mangy A Wu's appetite, and he started hatching schemes of his own while responding: "Fine, fine!"

The treasure hunter reached in his pocket but found that he did not have enough silver with him.

"Sir, we'll make a deal," he said to Mangy A Wu, "I'm going to get the silver right now and I'll be back around dusk to pick up the cat." And so saying, he put on his mended boot and hurried off.

Mangy A Wu waited until the treasure hunter was out of sight, then turned around and said to the cobbler: "Old man, lend your cat to me for a while. I'll give it back to you as soon as the jade mice are caught."

The old cobbler grabbed hold of his cat.

"At first, I just couldn't bear to part with my cat. Now I feel sorry for the twelve jade mice too. Treasures belong to everybody. You should leave them alone. What right have you to go capture them?"

Mangy A Wu became angry at this, so he pushed up his sleeves and pounced on the old cobbler. He beat the old man with his fists until he passed out and fell to the ground. The bully then picked up the cat and ran off with a victorious shout.

Darkness came. Mangy A Wu, drunk as a lord, stumbled and swayed to the Qiantang River bank with the cat in his arms. He climbed up the hill to the foot of Six Harmonies Pagoda, and waited until midnight when the moon was high

Su Dongpo Solves a Case by Painting Fans

up in the sky. He raised his head to look: Ah, yes indeed, there were twelve bright and shining jade mice jumping back and forth, frolicking on top of the pagoda. He quickly turned the cat loose. It was very strange: This cat, who ordinarily only closed its eyes to sleep, now suddenly appeared very alert. It perked up its ears, arched its back and stiffened its tail. It kept blinking its eyes, looking for all the world like a little tiger who had just come out of the mountains. It mewed a few times in the direction of the pagoda, then jumped right up to the top.

When the jade mice saw the Golden Silk Cat, they were so frightened that one by one they all fell off the top and were smashed to pieces. When Mangy A Wu rushed over, he did not see the jade mice so he thought they all ran away. He rushed over to catch them. Since he was drunk and his head was muddled, he rushed too fast, slipped, rolled downhill, and fell "plop" into the Qiantang River.

Now let's get back to the treasure hunter: When he had fetched the silver from home, he first made a detour to the market and bought a large net and a large bundle of cotton before he finally returned to the old cobbler's to get the cat. When he arrived, he found the old man unconscious on the ground, and no sign of the Golden Silk Cat. He gave it a moment's thought and realized that Mangy A Wu must have beat him to the punch. Quickly he ran towards the Qiantang River bank.

It turned out that he had not been totally forthright with Mangy: He had only told him what the Golden Silk Cat could do, but he had not taught him exactly how to catch the jade mice. To catch the jade mice, you have to first set up the net and put a lot of cotton on it, and only then can you let the cat out. In this way, when the jade mice fall, they will not be smashed.

By the time the treasure hunter had raced to the pagoda,

the jade mice had already been smashed and Mangy A Wu had died in the river. When he saw this, he stamped his feet and sighed in regret. However, what had happened had happened, and he had to admit his bad luck. He picked up his net and cotton, and left.

From then on, there have been no more jade mice on top of Six Harmonies Pagoda.

The bridge beside the old cobbler's, because of what had happened there, has since been called "Cat Bridge."

Su Dongpo Solves a Case
by Painting Fans

Su Dongpo (Su Shi, 1037-1101) was coming to Hangzhou to take up the position of Governor. As the news spread, a throng of people gathered in front of the yamen every day, waiting to have a look at the notice of his arrival, which would be posted on red paper, and to hear the three cannon shots that would announce his taking up office. However, they waited and waited and still saw no sign of his arrival.

One day, two people came to the yamen, yelling and fighting, and banged loudly on the drum to signify that there was a legal matter to be resolved and that they were going to charge each other with wrong doing.

The yamen runner came out and shouted: "Our new master has not yet arrived. If you have a court case, you'd better come back in two days!"

The two people, at the peak of their anger, both ignored the yamen runner and rushed into the yamen. Just at this point, a small donkey turned into the yamen from outside. Sitting on the donkey was a stout chap, wearing a soft hat and a loose robe. The dark tanned face was covered by a full beard.

As the donkey came in, the chap was muttering: "Make way, make way! I'm late!"

The donkey threaded its way through the crowd and walked directly into the yamen. The runner rushed forth to try to catch hold of the donkey's tail but he was one step too late, and the man headed straight into the yamen office.

This stout fellow tied his small donkey to the post, walked directly into the office and settled himself on the Tiger Chair.

The door guard, thinking this was a mad man, ran after him, shouting: "Hey! This is a Tiger Chair. Your head can be chopped off for just sitting on it!"

The man laughed loudly: "Ah! That bad?"

"Of course! Only those with a gold seal may sit on the Tiger Chair!"

"Oh, I have one of those things too." The stout fellow fetched out a shining gold seal from his pocket and put it on the desk.

When the door guard saw this, he was so shocked that his tongue dangled out to a length of three inches and could not be retracted for a long time. As it happened, this fellow was none other than the new Governor himself!

Su Dongpo arrived in such a hurry that he did not have time to post the notice or to have cannon shots fired. As soon as he arrived, he held court and had the two men brought in.

He rapped the gavel: "What are your names? Who is the plaintiff?"

The two men dropped to their knees and one of them said: "I am the plaintiff and my name is Li Xiaoyi."

"And my name is Hong A Mao."

"Li Xiaoyi, why are you suing him?"

"I saved up ten ounces of silver from doing odd jobs and

two months ago I lent it to Hong A Mao to start a business. We were close neighbors so I told him that I would not charge him any interest, but that any time I might need it, he had to give it back to me. Now I have found myself a bride and I am waiting for my money so I can get married. Not only would he not give me back my money, the man even beat me!"

"Why did you beat him when you are still in his debt?" Su Dongpo turned around and asked Hong A Mao.

Hong A Mao immediately kowtowed and explained: "Your Honor! Sir! I'm just a man doing seasonal business with very small capital. I used the money I borrowed from him to buy some fans before the summer solstice. Who could have known that it would still be quite cool even after the Dragon-boat Festival! People are still wearing heavy clothing. Who would buy my fans? It has been overcast and rainy these few days and the fans in my trunk are all getting mouldy! I really have no silver to give back to him, and he started to curse me and press me. I guess I just became exasperated and hit him. I did not do it on purpose!"

Su Dongpo wrinkled his brow: "Li Xiaoyi's marriage is important. Hong A Mao should return his ten ounces of silver immediately."

Hong A Mao started to yell: "Your Honor! I simply do not have the silver to repay him!"

Su Dongpo tugged at his beard: "Hong A Mao has lost money in his business. Things are hard for him. Li Xiaoyi must think of some other way to get the money for his marriage."

Li Xiaoyi shouted his complaint: "Your Honor! It was no easy matter for me to save up that ten ounces of silver!"

Su Dongpo smiled: "You needn't worry. Now, Hong A Mao, you go home and bring back twenty of the moulding paper fans to me and we'll solve this case."

Hong A Mao was delighted at this. He scrambled up and shot back home. He brought back twenty white folding fans and gave them to Su Dongpo, who unfolded them one by one and lay them on his desk. He prepared some ink and soaked his writing brush in it. He started to paint rocks and potted plants on those with large mould stains, and pine trees, bamboo and plums on those with small stains. Within a very short time, he finished painting all twenty folding fans.

He gave ten of them to Li Xiaoyi: "The ten ounces of silver you need to get married is all on these fans. You take them outside and call: 'Su Dongpo's paintings. One ounce of silver for a fan.' You will sell them in no time."

Then he gave ten fans to Hong A Mao: "You also take these and sell them outside the yamen. When you get ten ounces of silver, you can start another business."

The two men took the fans but both were doubtful of what Su Dongpo said. However, once outside they yelled only twice and the twenty fans were gone in no time. Li Xiaoyi and Hong A Mao went home happily with ten ounces of beautiful shining silver.

This anecdote of "Su Dongpo solving a case by painting fans" has been passed on from person to person, and people still talk about it even today.

Dongpo Meat

W hen Su Dongpo was the Governor of Hangzhou, he had West Lake dredged and by so doing did a good deed for the people.

After West Lake had been dredged, the fields around it were no longer threatened by flood or draught. In this particular year, the winds and rain were just right in Hangzhou and there was a bumper harvest all around the area. Everyone was grateful to Su Dongpo for the good deed of dredging West Lake, so, many people brought him pork and wine at New Year to offer as a token of their gratitude.

Su Dongpo accepted a lot of pork and had it cut into squares, then had the squares cooked until red and tender. He had these sent to the families of those who had dredged the lake, giving one piece to each family according to the name list of the workers. It had been a good year; each and every household was already happy! On top of this, they now enjoyed the meat which Su Dongpo sent, and they were even happier. The old folks laughed, the young ones danced about and everyone praised Su Dongpo for being such a good and "fatherly" official. They called the meat that Su Dongpo sent them "Dongpo meat."

At that time there was a big restaurant in Hangzhou, and when the proprietor heard that people were praising this "Dongpo meat," he discussed it with his chef. They decided to cut their pork into squares and to cook it to a tender red. They hung out a sign advertising "Dongpo meat."

As soon as this restaurant came up with this new dish, its business really thrived. Customers came continually from morning till night. They had to kill ten pigs every day and even that was not quite enough. The proprietors of other restaurants became envious and soon started learning to make "Dongpo meat." Later on, the restaurateurs had a meeting and decided to make "Dongpo meat" Hangzhou's number one dish.

Su Dongpo was an upright person who would never cower before the noble and powerful, so all the sly officials in court hated him. Now when they saw that he was loved and respected by the people of Hangzhou, they became very uneasy. Among them was s censor who decided to go to Hangzhou in disguise, hoping to find some fault with Su Dongpo so as to do him in.

The first day the censor arrived in Hangzhou, he came to a restaurant for lunch, and the waiter brought him the menu. When he looked at the menu, he found that the first dish on the list was none other than "Dongpo meat"! First, he wrinkled his brow in thought, then he became very happy, slapping the table top and shouting: "I want this dish!"

When he tried the meat, he found it was indeed delicious; and by questioning the waiter he learned that the restaurant operators had decided to make it the number one dish of Hangzhou. Thereupon, he collected menus from all the restaurants and went back to the capital, feeling elated.

As soon as the censor was back in the capital city, he went to see the Emperor.

"Your Majesty! Su Dongpo is breaking laws and accepting all kinds of bribes as Governor of Hangzhou. He has committed every evil you can imagine and the people there all hate him so much that everyone would have him cooked and eaten."

"How do you know that? What evidence do you have?" The Emperor asked.

Thereupon, the censor presented all the greasy menus he had collected. This Emperor was not particularly bright, so when he saw the menus, he immediately issued an Imperial Edict ordering Su Dongpo discharged and banished to far away Hainan Island to serve in the army.

Even after he was discharged from office, the people of Hangzhou could not forget the good things Su Dongpo had done, and they all praised and respected him as they had before. Thus, "Dongpo meat" has been handed down from generation to generation, and even today it is still the number one dish in Hangzhou.

Oil Fried Hui

O il fried fritters used to be called "oil fried Hui," and it is said that they were first made by the people of Hangzhou.

During the Southern Song Dynasty, the treacherous Prime Minister Qin Hui and his wife Madame Wang, plotting in private chambers, had the loyal general Yue Fei burnt alive in the Wind Wave Pavilion. When the news spread around, people everywhere were indignant and angry. Everyone in the restaurants and teahouses, in the streets and alleys, was talking about this.

At this time, there were two food stalls set up side by side beneath Public Safety Bridge: one of them sold sesame seed flatcakes while the other sold oil fried sweet rice fritters. One day, just as the morning rush was over, Wang Er, who sold the flatcakes, lowered his fire. As he tidied things up, he noticed that there were no more customers so he sat down to take a break. At the same time Li Si, the seller of sweet rice fritters, also tidied up his pot of oil and squatted down to puff on his pipe. They said hello to each other, then Li Si came walking over and they both sat down and started to chat. Chatting on and on, they started to talk about Qin Hui's killing of Yue Fei.

As they talked they became so angry that finally Li Si could contain himself no longer. Pounding his fist on the bench, he shouted: "The traitor! I'd like to ...!"

Hearing this, Wang Er smiled: "Brother Li, here's how I'd take care of them!" So saying, he picked up two lumps of dough from his counter and started to knead and shape them. Eventually he had made two figures: One was a large person with slanted eye-brows and the other was a woman with lips puckered. He picked up his knife and chopped the neck of the big figure with slanted eye-brows, then gave a straight thrust through the stomach of the woman with puckered lips.

"What do you think of that?" He asked Li Si.

Li Si nodded his head: "But this is still too easy on them!" And so saying, he ran back to his own stall and brought his pot of oil over to Wang Er's stove. Then he reshaped the sliced figures, stuck them to each other back to back, and threw them into the pot of oil. As the figures were being fried, he shouted: "Everybody come and watch us oil fry Hui! Hey, everybody! Come to watch us oil fry Hui!"

When passers-by heard this, they became curious and crowded over to watch. When they saw the man and woman being deep-fried until they hissed, they seemed to understand what was going on. They were delighted and started to shout: "Look! See the oil fried Hui! See the oil fried Hui!"

At this very moment, they heard the banging of gongs, and they looked to discover that it was Qin Hui, seated in his eight-man sedan chair, just returning from the Imperial Court, and passing by Public Safety Bridge. When Qin Hui heard this racket, he suspected something foul was afoot, so he stopped his sedan chair and ordered his guards to arrest the trouble makers. The guards pushed through the crowd, arrested Wang Er and Li Si, and confiscated the oil pot.

When Qin Hui saw the two black figures in the pot of oil, he was so furious that his entire beard bristled. He stepped down from his sedan chair and shouted: "How dare you! Is this some sort of rebellion?"

Wang Er smiled and replied calmly: "We are just small business men. How could we rebel?"

"Well then why are you using my tabooed name like this?"

Wang Er replied: "Ah, Prime Minister, Your Honor! The 'hui' we are using is different from yours!"

At this point, the crowd joined in, shouting: "That's right! The same sound, but a different character!"

Qin Hui was stumped.

He took a look at the two blackened figures floating in the oil and shouted: "Rubbish! How could anyone eat this charcoal! It is clear that you two sly devils are stirring up trouble behind the government's back!"

Hearing this, two people stepped out from the crowd: "No! This is the right way to fry them. This is the only way to fry them!" And so saying, they picked up the fried dough, broke it in two and popped it into their mouths. As they munched on it, they exclaimed: "Mmm, delicious! The more you eat, the more you want to eat. Makes you want to swallow it in one gulp!"

Now this put Qin Hui in an embarrassing position, and he could do nothing but give them an angry glare. He slipped back into the sedan chair and went away without a word.

The great Prime Minister had lost face in front of the general public and this immediately became the hottest news in Hangzhou. People came to Public Safety Bridge in droves to have a taste of this "oil fried Hui." Li Si decided to abandon his sweet rice fritters and moved his oil pot over to Wang Er's stall. They merged into one stall and started selling "oil fried Hui."

At first, "oil fried Hui" was made of two figures stuck together back to back, but this way they had to shape the figures one by one and this took too much time and was a waste of labor. Later on, Wang Er and Li Si thought of an easier way. They rolled a large piece of dough until it was flat, then cut it into several small strips. They took two of these, one as Qin Hui, the other as Madame Wang, pressed them together with a rolling pin, then twisted them together. These were fried in the pot of oil and still called "oil fried Hui." This was a much more convenient way to make them.

At first, people ate "oil fried Hui" to express their hatred for Qin Hui. However, it turned out that they were quite good and also cheap, so more and more people started to eat them. Soon other stalls started to imitate them and began selling "oil fried Hui," until eventually this food spread all over the country.

It was from that time that "oil fried Hui" became a favorite food among the people. Later on, owing to the fact that "oil fried Hui" were made in strips, they started calling them "oil fried fritters."

Oil fried fritters were first made at a flatcake stall, and this custom has been preserved, so that even today flatcakes and oil fried fritters are still made at a single stall.

List of Motifs

Motif-index		**West Lake Folktales**
A1111.	Impounded water (water is kept by monster, released by hero)	The First Well Spring of Mount Wu
A1115.	Why the sea is salty	Beating the Dragon King
A1125.	Winds caused by flapping wings/sleeves	A Thread of Sky
A1131.	Origin of rain	A Thread of Sky
A1141.6.	Lightning produced by deity	A Thread of Sky
A1142.0.1.	Origin of thunderbolt	A Thread of Sky
A1510.	Origin of eating customs	Dongpo Meat; Oil Fried Hui
A2441.	(Causes of) animal's gait or walk	Lady White
A2681.	Origin of trees	Laurel Peak
A2681.9.	Origin of mulberry tree	Lady Silkworm
B11.	Dragon	The Bright Pearl; The Little Yellow Dragon; Jade Spring; The Black Dragon; The Hua Pond; The First Well Spring of Mount Wu
B11.2.10.	Scales of Dragon	The Little Yellow Dragon
B11.2.11.	Fire-breathing dragon	The Little Yellow Dragon
B11.5.1.	Dragon's power of self-transformation	The Little Yellow Dragon
B11.12.5.	The dragon king	Six Harmonies Tries to Fill the River; Beating the Dragon King
B32.	Phoenix	The Bright Pearl; Rising Sun Terrace; Phoenix Mountain
B102.	Animal of precious metal (jewels)	Cat Bridge
B103.2.1.	Treasure-laying bird	Phoenix Mountain

	Motif-index	West Lake Folktales
B181.1.	Magic cat	Cat Bridge
B200.	Animals with human traits	Monkey Calling Cave
C833.	Tabus for journeys	Rising Sun Terrace
D169.	Transformation: man/ woman to bird – miscellaneous	A Thread of Sky
D199.2.	Transformation: man to dragon	The Black Dragon
D391.	Transformation: serpent to person	Lady White
D399.	Transformation: other animals to person	The Little Yellow Dragon
D399.1.	Transformation: water- dragon to person	Jade Spring
D810.	Magic object a gift	Xing Chan
D811.1.	Magic object received from goddess	Xing Chan
D1072.2.	Magic hairpin	Xing Chan
D1390.	Magic object rescues person	Xing Chan
E1.	Person comes to life	Lady White; Six Harmonies Tries to Fill the River
F210.	Fairyland	Lady Silkworm
F236.13.	Fairies in white clothes	Lady Silkworm
F240.	Possessions of fairies	Lady Silkworm
F260.	Behavior of fairies	Lady Silkworm
F337.	Fairy grateful to mortal for saving his/her life	Lady Silkworm
F530.	Exceptionally large or small men	Rising Sun Terrace; Beating the Dragon King
F800.	Extraordinary rocks and stones	Plum Blossom Monument

Motif-index		West Lake Folktales
F934.	Extraordinary occurrences connected with lakes	Golden Ox Lake
F950.	Marvelous cures	Immortal Gazing Bridge
H506.	Test of resourcefulness	Xing Chan
H580.	(Riddles) Enigmatic statements	Lady White
H1233.6.2.	Bird helper on quest	Rising Sun Terrace
H1370.	Miscellaneous quests	Rising Sun Terrace
H1502.	Test: enduring hardship	Stone Man Ridge
J1179.	Clever judicial decisions — miscellaneous	Su Dongpo Solves a Case by Painting Fans
J1192.	The bribed judge	Immortal Gazing Bridge
J1254.	Evading a direct answer which may trap one	Monk Censure Teases Emperor Qianlong
J2420.	Foolish imitation — miscellaneous	The Beancurd Bridges
J2650.	Bungling fool	Emperor Kangxi Inscribes a Plaque
K250.	Other deceptive bargains	The Stone Censer; Jade Spring
K1812.17.	King in disguise to spy out his kingdom	Monk Censure Teases Emperor Qianlong
K2000.	Hypocrites	Eight-trigram Plot
K2060.	Detection of hypocrisy	Eight-trigram Plot
K2100.	False accusation	Dongpo Meat
K2248.	Treacherous minister	The Foul Qin Hui; Oil Fried Hui
M411.	Deliverer of curse	Six Harmonies Tries to Fill the River
M414.13.	Curse on a deity	Six Harmonies Tries to Fill the River
P253.8.	Clever sister saves life of brother	Phoenix Mountain
P453.	Shoemaker	Cat Bridge

Motif-index		West Lake Folktales
Q111.3.	Riches as reward (of hospitality)	Phoenix Mountain; The Ancestors of Tea
Q250.	Unkindness punished	The Hua Pond
R9.1.	Sun captured	Rising Sun Terrace
T111.	Marriage of mortal and super-natural being	Lady White
W28.	Self-sacrifice	Rising Sun Terrace; The Little Yellow Dragon; Stone Man Ridge; The First Well Spring of Mount Wu
X410.	Jokes on parsons	Yuchi Gong and the Monk
Z71.1.	Formulistic number: three	The First Well Spring of Mount Wu

List of Place Names

Arranged alphabetically according to English translation, indicating also where they first appear in the stories

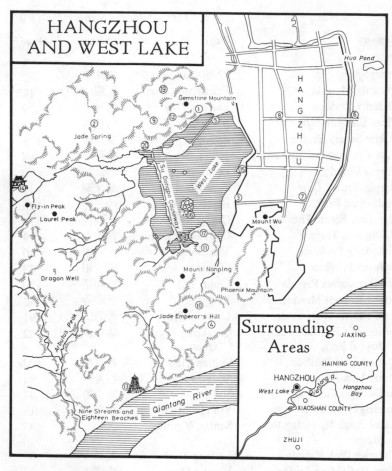

HANGZHOU AND WEST LAKE

Gemstone Mountain
Jade Spring
Fly-in Peak
Laurel Peak
Dragon Well
Arbutus Peak
Nine Streams and Eighteen Beaches
Su Dongpo Causeway
West Lake
Mount Wu
Mount Nanping
Phoenix Mountain
Jade Emperor's Hill
Qiantang River
Hua Pond

H A N G Z H O U

Surrounding Areas

JIAXING
HAINING COUNTY
HANGZHOU
West Lake
Qiantang R.
Hangzhou Bay
XIAOSHAN COUNTY
ZHUJI

1	Bao Chu Pagoda	11	Pure Compassion Monastery
2	Clear Ripple Temple	12	Rising Sun Terrace
3	Clear Wave Gate	13	Six Harmonies Pagoda
4	Eight-trigram Plot	14	Soul's Retreat Monastery
5	Interrupting Bridge	15	Surging Gold Gate
6	Jubilant Spring Gate	16	Three Pools Mirroring the Moon
7	Plum Blossom Monument	17	Thunder Peak Pagoda
8	Public Safety Bridge	18	Wave Reflecting Bridge
9	Purple Cloud Cave	19	Yellow Dragon Cave
10	Purple Source Cave	20	Yue Tomb

The Translators

Jan W. Walls received his B.A., M.A. and Ph. D. degrees in Chinese language and literature from Indiana University. He has published English translations of Chinese poetry in various journals and anthologies, and written several articles on Chinese writers, Chinese literature, and literary translation. He collaborated with his wife, Yvonne, in the Chinese translation of John Steinbeck's *Cannery Row,* and in English translations of poetry by Li Ying, and portions of the novel *The Glittering Red Star.* He has been teaching Chinese language and literature since 1970, and is currently Associate Professor and Director of the Center for Pacific and Oriental Studies at the University of Victoria, B.C., Canada.

Yvonne Ying Li Walls is a native of Jinzhou, Liaoning Province. She received her B.A. degree in English from Taiwan Normal University, her M. A. in Comparative Literature from the University of Washington, and did post-graduate work at Indiana University. She has published articles both in Chinese and English, and has translated English poetry and short stories into Chinese, and edited and annotated *Selected Poems of Thomas Hardy.* She is co-translator of John Steinbeck's *Cannery Row* into Chinese, and of selected poems by Li Ying and portions of *The Glittering Red Star* into English. At present, she is doing translations and teaching part-time at the University of Victoria, B.C., Canada.

The Illustrator

Cheng Shifa is one of the leading masters of the modern art of illustrations in China. From the 1950's onwards he created numerous sets of drawings based on famous novels which won him nationwide acclaim. These works include *Wild Boar Forest* (an extract from *Water Margin*), *Ballad of Bravery and Swords* and *The True Story of Ah Q in Pictures*.

Cheng is also expert in Chinese ink and wash painting, especially in depicting ethnic minority groups. Learning from great masters of the past like Chen Laolian and Ren Bonian he explores modern ways of artistic representation. Fine brushwork and the splash-ink technique are both employed to produce detailed features against a background of subtle colors. The illustrations for this book are fine examples of his style.